Nonfiction Reading Comprehension

1-2

Written by
Christine Dugan

D1223899

Editors: Carla Hamaguchi and Collene Dobelmann
Illustrator: Jenny Campbell
Designer/Production: Moonhee Pak/Andrea Ables
Cover Designer: Barbara Peterson
Art Director: Tom Cochrane
Project Director: Carolea Williams

Table of Contents

Introduction

Each book in the *Power Practice*™ series contains dozens of ready-to-use activity pages to provide students with skill practice. Use the fun activities to supplement and enhance what you are already teaching in your classroom. Give an activity page to students as independent class work, or send the pages home as homework to reinforce skills taught in class. An answer key is provided for quick reference.

Nonfiction Reading Comprehension 1–2 features grade-level nonfiction reading selections and follow-up activities. The activities include using context clues, summarizing, vocabulary development, using graphic organizers, making inferences, using prior knowledge to make personal connections, structural patterns, questioning, main idea, factual recall, comparing and contrasting, cause and effect, and main idea.

In the first half of the book, each passage and follow-up activity appear on one page. The latter half of the book contains longer passages. These passages are on one page and two separate follow-up activities accompany each passage.

Use the ready-to-go activities to "recharge" skill review and give students the power to succeed!

All About Whales

What do you know about whales?

All whales are **mammals**, just like us! They have hair and they are warm-blooded. They breathe air into their lungs through a small hole called a blowhole.

Whales swim many miles each year. They often move in groups called **pods**.

Did you know that whales can also sing? Whales make a whistling sound that can sound like a song. Some whales can be heard from miles away.

Whales are very interesting animals!

Read each sentence. Circle the word or words that make the sentence true.

1 Whales are mammals with _____.
   hair
   a shell

2 Whales often swim in groups called _____.
   pods
   herds

3 Whales breathe air into _____.
   lungs
   gills

4 All whales are _____.
   cold-blooded
   warm-blooded

Name _____   Date _____

Whale Facts

There are many different kinds of whales. The biggest whale is the blue whale. It can grow to be almost 100 feet long. That is as long as three school buses! The blue whale is the largest animal on Earth.

The humpback whale is smaller than the blue whale. It grows to be about 50 feet long. Humpback whales love to swim. They like to jump out of the water. They get their name from the way they move their back when they dive.

The killer whale, or **orca**, is even smaller than the humpback whale. It grows to be about 30 feet long. Orcas are mostly black with some white spots. Orcas eat different kinds of fish. They will even attack and eat young whales!

Different kinds of whales have many things in common. Each kind of whale is also very different.

Compare the three kinds of whales. Write one fact that you learned about each whale in the boxes.

Blue Whale	**Humpback Whale**	**Killer Whale**
_____ _____ _____	_____ _____ _____	_____ _____ _____

Nonfiction Reading Comprehension • 1–2 © 2005 Creative Teaching Press

Fun in the Water

Whales move in the water in different ways. They may be playing or looking around. They may be warning other whales about something.

Have you ever seen a picture of a whale flipping out of the water? When whales jump high out of the water, it is called **breaching**.

Whales poke their head out of the water and turn around. This is called **spyhopping**.

Some whales stick their tail out of the water. They might slap it on the water and make a loud sound. This is called **lobtailing**.

Whales are interesting to watch!

What does a whale look like when it is breaching, spyhopping, or lobtailing? Draw a picture of each activity.

Breaching

Spyhopping		**Lobtailing**

Make a Snack

Fruit is good for you! How do you make a fruit salad?

First, wash the fruit so it is clean. Then, peel the fruit if you need to. Some fruit, such as an apple, has a skin that you can eat. Next, cut the fruit into small pieces. Ask an adult to help you use a knife. Finally, mix the fruit together in a bowl. Eat and enjoy your treat!

How do you make a fruit salad? Put the steps in order. Number them from 1 to 4.

_____ Cut the fruit.

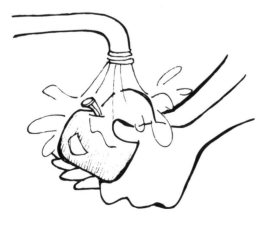

_____ Mix the fruit.

_____ Wash the fruit.

_____ Peel the fruit.

Nonfiction Reading Comprehension • 1–2 © 2005 Creative Teaching Press

Healthy Foods

It is important to eat good foods every day. Good foods keep your body healthy. Fruits, like apples and bananas, are healthy foods. Fruits have vitamins and minerals that your body needs to grow.

Vegetables are also good to eat. Vegetables have vitamins and minerals that your body needs. What kind of vegetables do you eat every day?

Your health is very important. It is smart to take care of your body—no matter how old you are!

Draw pictures of the healthy foods you like to eat.

From Farm to Home

How do we get the food we eat? Have you thought about how food gets to your table?

Much of our food comes from farms. Some farmers grow food, like apples and corn. Other farmers take care of cows that give us milk and cheese. Chickens live on farms and give us eggs and meat.

Trucks, ships, and planes help move food from farms to stores. We buy our food in the store. The food we eat may come from far away.

Look at your lunch or dinner. Where do you think your food came from?

Draw pictures to show how food gets from the farm to your home.

Food is grown on farms.

Trucks, ships, and planes help move food to the store.

We buy food at the store.

We eat food at home.

Nonfiction Reading Comprehension • 1–2 © 2005 Creative Teaching Press

Name _____   Date _____

All About Butterflies

Butterflies are insects. There are many different kinds of butterflies. They live in all parts of the world.

Butterflies have six legs and three body parts. The three body parts are the head, thorax, and abdomen. The **thorax** is also called the chest. The **abdomen** is the tail end of the butterfly.

Butterflies use their wings to fly. Their wings have to be warm to fly. They will use the sun to warm up their wings.

Have you ever seen a butterfly sitting on a flower? It is probably having lunch! Butterflies love to drink nectar from flowers.

There is a lot to learn about butterflies!

Answer the questions about butterflies.

1 What is the tail end of a butterfly called?

_____

2 How many legs do butterflies have?

_____

3 What do butterflies drink?

_____

4 Where do butterflies live?

_____

5 What is another name for the thorax?

_____

Nonfiction Reading Comprehension • 1–2 © 2005 Creative Teaching Press

Butterfly Life Cycle

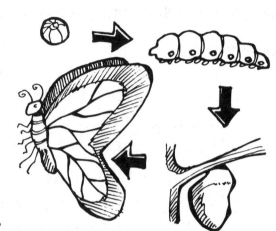

A butterfly changes many times during its life. First, a butterfly starts as an egg.

Then, a caterpillar hatches from the egg. This caterpillar is also called a larva. The **larva** eats a lot of food and gets bigger. The larva loses its skin as it grows.

Next, the larva turns into a pupa, or **chrysalis**. The pupa rests while it grows.

Finally, a butterfly flies out of the chrysalis. The butterfly is already an adult. This adult can lay an egg. The cycle starts all over again!

This passage tells about the life cycle of a butterfly in a special order. Fill in the blanks to tell what happens to a butterfly.

1 First, _____

_____.

2 Then, _____

_____.

3 Next, _____

_____.

4 Finally, _____

_____.

Nonfiction Reading Comprehension • 1–2 © 2005 Creative Teaching Press

Name _____ Date _____

Monarch Butterflies

What do you know about monarch butterflies? What do you want to know? Fill in the first two columns of the KWL chart before you read the passage.

One kind of butterfly is called a monarch butterfly. It has colorful wings that are orange and black. It also has white spots.

Monarch butterflies live all over the world. Some monarchs stay in one place their entire lives. Other monarchs migrate. Migrate means to move from place to place. Monarchs may migrate over 2,000 miles!

Monarchs love to eat a plant called milkweed. They eat the leaves of the plant. Monarchs also lay their eggs on the leaves. Then caterpillars have food right when they come out of the egg.

Keep your eyes open for this beautiful insect flying outside!

Now that you've read about monarch butterflies, fill in the last column of the KWL chart.

What You **K**now	What You **W**ant to Know	What You **L**earned

Nonfiction Reading Comprehension • 1–2 © 2005 Creative Teaching Press

Name _____ Date _____

Your Five Senses

Think about eating an apple. You use all of your five senses when you eat an apple.

First, you use your eyes to see the apple. Is it red or green? Then, you use your hand to touch the apple. How does it feel? You take a bite to taste the apple. How does it taste? You listen as you take a bite. What sounds do you hear when you take a bite? You can smell the apple as you eat it. Does it smell sweet?

Think about how you use your five senses every day. Your five senses help you learn about the world around you.

Which parts of your body do you use when you use your five senses? Draw pictures that show what helps you see, feel, taste, hear, and smell.

See	**Feel**	**Taste**

Hear	**Smell**

Your Heart

The heart is very important. What does your heart do inside of you?

Your heart is inside your chest. It is about the size of a fist. The heart is a muscle. It pumps blood to the rest of your body.

Doctors listen to your heart. They want to make sure it is working well.

Your heart works hard to keep you healthy. Put your hand on your chest. Can you feel your heart beating? It is working right now!

1 What is the main idea of the passage you just read? Circle your choice.

The heart is the size of a fist.

The heart is very important and it works hard to keep you healthy.

The heart is a muscle.

Doctors listen to your heart.

2 Why do doctors listen to your heart?

_____

3 Put your hand on your heart. Count how many times your heart beats in 10 seconds. Write the number.

_____

Nonfiction Reading Comprehension • 1–2 © 2005 Creative Teaching Press

Your Teeth

Smile and show your teeth!

We have different kinds of teeth. Some teeth are sharp so that we can cut food. Other teeth are more flat so that we can crush food. Some teeth help us to chew food.

Have you ever been to the dentist? Dentists help you take care of your teeth. They want you to brush your teeth every day.

You get your first tooth when you are a baby. When you grow up, you have 32 teeth. That is a lot of teeth to brush!

How do you take care of your teeth? Draw a picture in the box.

Nonfiction Reading Comprehension • 1–2 © 2005 Creative Teaching Press

Name _____ Date _____

Your Skeleton and Bones

What would happen if you had no bones? You would be a pile of skin on the floor! Bones helps us stand up and move around. Bones also help protect important body parts inside of us.

You were born with 300 bones. Some of those bones join together. When you grow up, you will only have 206 bones! The largest bone in your body is your thigh bone, which is in your leg. The smallest bone is inside your ear.

How can you keep the bones in your body strong? One way is to eat foods that have **calcium**. Calcium is a mineral found in foods like milk and cheese. Another way to take care of your bones is to exercise. Playing soccer and running are examples of good ways to exercise.

Feel your arm or leg. Can you feel the bones in your own body?

Read each sentence. Fill in the bubble next to the word or words that make the sentence true.

1 You were born with _____ bones.
○ 350   ○ 206   ○ 300

2 Bones help us to _____.
○ breathe   ○ smell   ○ stand up and move around

3 Eating foods that have _____ will help make your bones strong.
○ bones   ○ calcium   ○ good smells

4 The smallest bone in your body is _____.
○ in your nose   ○ inside your ear   ○ in your finger

Name _____ Date _____

Maps

Why do we use maps? Maps can tell us where we are located or where we want to go!

There can be many different maps of one place. For example, one map of your town may show streets and roads. Another map of your town may show where mountains or lakes are located.

You need to know the four directions to read a map. North, south, east, and west are labels on most maps. North is usually at the top of a map.

Maps often have symbols to show different things. For example, a river may look like a blue line on a map. A city may look like a dot. Most maps explain their symbols in a **legend**, or key.

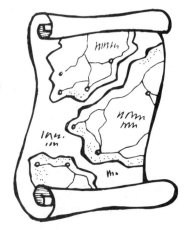

Maps can be on paper, on the computer, on television, or in other forms. When was the last time you saw a map?

Draw a map of a place you know. For example, you can draw your classroom or your room at home. Make sure to include a key if you use symbols.

Name _____ Date _____

South America

Earth has both land and water. Earth's land is divided into large pieces. These pieces are called <u>continents</u>.

South America is one of the seven continents on Earth. It has 12 countries. The Amazon River is in South America. It is one of the longest rivers in the world.

The Amazon River is <u>unique</u> because it is actually four colors! Different parts of the river have white, black, blue, and brown water. The <u>mouth</u> of the Amazon River is at the Atlantic Ocean. This is where the river ends.

South America <u>borders</u> three oceans. On one side is the Pacific Ocean. On the other side is the Atlantic Ocean. The Southern Ocean also touches South America.

There are many interesting facts to learn about South America!

What new words did you learn while reading about South America? Draw a line to match each word to its meaning. Remember to use context clues.

Continent means   touches.

Unique means   the end of the river.

Mouth means   a large piece of land.

Borders means   interesting and different.

Name _____ Date _____

State Capitals

Where is your state capital? Every state has its own capital. The capital is the city where the governor works. The governor is the leader of the state. The capital usually has a large building where the governor works.

Many people help make your state a nice place to live. They all work in the capital city. They work on making better schools. They help keep parks, lakes, and streets clean. They take care of all the roads in your state. They also make sure cities are safe.

Capitals are very interesting places to visit. Have you been to your capital city?

Austin, Texas ☆

What do you know about your state capital or your governor? Draw a picture in the box.

Fire Safety

Keep a cool head if you are ever in a fire. You should practice what to do in a fire at school or at home.

Make sure you know how to exit your school or home. Learn a few different ways to get out in case one exit is blocked by fire. Don't ever hide during a fire.

If fire gets on your clothes, do three things. STOP what you are doing. DROP to the floor. ROLL around until the fire is out.

Make sure that your house has a fire alarm. It will make a loud noise if there is smoke or fire inside. This will let you know that you need to go outside.

Talk to your teacher and the adults at home to learn more that you can do in a fire.

Read the sentences. Look at the underlined word or words. What other word or words mean the same thing? Write the sentence again on the line. Use the new word or words.

1 Make sure you know how to <u>exit</u> your school or home.

_____

2 It will make a loud <u>noise</u> if there is smoke or fire inside.

_____

3 <u>Keep a cool head</u> if you are ever in a fire.

_____

4 Talk to your teacher and the <u>adults at home</u> to learn more that you can do in a fire.

_____

Bicycle Safety

It is important to take care of yourself when you ride a bike. How can you stay safe?

First, always wear a helmet! Keep your head safe.

Second, check your bike to make sure it works well. Look for flat tires or parts that don't work.

Third, follow the rules of the road. Ride your bike in safe areas.

Finally, watch for cars, bumps, rocks, and other things you may run over.

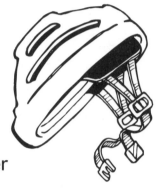

Think about the four rules. What might happen if you did **NOT** follow them? Draw a picture in each box.

<u>Rules</u>	If you don't . . .
1 Wear a helmet. ⟶	
2 Check your bike. ⟶	
3 Follow the rules of the road. ⟶	
4 Watch for cars, bumps, and other things. ⟶	

Nonfiction Reading Comprehension • 1–2 © 2005 Creative Teaching Press

Name _____ Date _____

Spiders

There are many different kinds of spiders. They live in all parts of the world. Spiders come in many colors. You can find black, brown, red, and green spiders!

All spiders have eight legs. Each leg has two or three claws at the end. A spider's body is made up of two parts. Spiders have very strong jaws.

Spiders make webs out of silk. Many spiders trap their food in the web. Spiders are **carnivores**. Carnivores like to eat meat.

If you see a spider, watch out! It might be a jumping spider. Jumping spiders like to jump on fingers!

Use words you learned about spiders to complete the crossword puzzle.

Across
2. Spiders live in all parts of the _____.
4. Spiders can be black, brown, red, or _____.
6. A spider's body is made up of _____ parts.

Down
1. Spiders eat with strong _____.
3. All spiders have eight _____.
5. Spiders are carnivores so they eat _____.

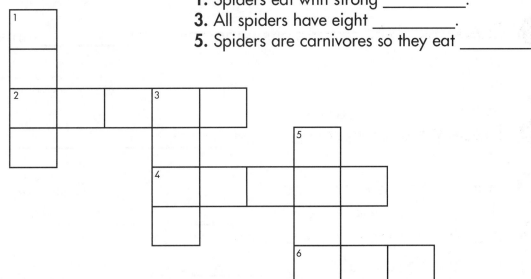

Nonfiction Reading Comprehension • 1–2 © 2005 Creative Teaching Press

Hummingbirds

Hummingbirds may be tiny birds, but they can do interesting things!

Hummingbirds can fly in any direction. They can move up, down, or to the side. They can even fly upside down! Hummingbirds can also stay in one place in midair. This is called **hovering**.

A hummingbird can flap its wings over 50 times in a single second! Hummingbirds work hard when they move, so they have to eat every 10 minutes. Hummingbirds eat tiny bugs. They also eat nectar from flowers.

A hummingbird has to be careful of bigger birds. Some large birds eat hummingbirds!

What facts did you learn about hummingbirds? Fill in the blanks.

1 Hummingbirds eat _____ from flowers.

2 Hummingbirds eat every _____ minutes.

3 A hummingbird can flap its wings over _____ times in a single second.

4 When hummingbirds stay in one place in midair, it is called _____.

5 Hummingbirds can fly up, down, to the side, and even _____!

6 Hummingbirds eat tiny _____.

Nonfiction Reading Comprehension • 1–2 © 2005 Creative Teaching Press

Name _____   Date _____

Camels

What do you know about camels? There are many interesting facts to learn about camels.

Camels are mammals. They can live in deserts where it gets very hot. They can also live in places that get very cold.

Most people know that camels have humps on their back. They may have one or two humps. What is inside of the hump? Some people think water is in the hump. That is not true. The hump is full of fat. Camels can go with no food or water for a few days.

Camels also have long eyelashes. This helps protect their eyes from sand.

Find the words about camels in the word search.

camel	desert	eyelash	hot
hump	mammal	sand	water

C H R D U I S G A M

O H O T S A N D E A

C U T A L H A E L M

A M A D J O D S C M

M P L I K E U E I A

E Y E L A S H R A L

L A R I L W A T E R

Nonfiction Reading Comprehension • 1–2 © 2005 Creative Teaching Press

Ants

Ants may be small, but they sure are strong! Did you know that ants can lift something that is 20 times their own body weight? That means that if you weigh 40 pounds, you could lift 800 pounds!

Ants are insects that have six legs. They live in groups called **colonies**. Each colony has a queen. The queen ant lays eggs. Other ants take care of the eggs until they hatch.

Ants build their own homes, too. They dig underground tunnels for the other ants to go to rest, or hibernate.

Ants only live for one or two months, but they sure do a lot during their short lives!

Look at the graphic organizer. It lists four facts about ants. Add a detail you read under each fact.

Ants are strong.	Ants are insects.	Ants live in colonies.	Ants build their own homes.
_____ _____ _____	_____ _____ _____	_____ _____ _____	_____ _____ _____

Sharks

Sharks are a kind of fish. They live in every part of the world. There are many different kinds of sharks. Some live in cold water. Some live in warm water.

Many people think that sharks hunt humans. That is not really true. Many scientists feel that sharks bite humans because they think the humans are seals. Seals are a favorite food for many kinds of sharks! Did you know that sharks eat their food in whole pieces? They do not chew food. After eating a big seal or fish, sharks might not eat for another month or two.

Humans hurt sharks more than sharks hurt humans. It's important to know that shark attacks are very rare.

You have read many facts about sharks. Some people have opinions about sharks, too. Can you tell the difference? Read each statement. Write **F** if the statement is a fact or **O** if it is an opinion.

1. Sharks are very scary. _____

2. Sharks live in cold and warm water. _____

3. Sharks are mean animals. _____

4. Sharks like to eat seals. _____

5. Sharks eat their food in whole pieces. _____

6. Sharks should be captured if they are near a beach. _____

7. Sharks live in every part of the world. _____

Changing Seasons

Each year, the weather changes with the seasons. We have four seasons called fall, winter, spring, and summer.

It is fall when you start school. In fall, leaves on trees turn colors. Fall turns to winter, and rain or snow comes!

In winter, it is cold outside. You have to wear warm clothes.

In spring, flowers start to grow. The sun comes out and warms up everything.

Finally, in summer, we get to enjoy many sunny days. Sometimes it can be very hot in the summer!

What is your favorite season?

What did you learn about each season? Think about an activity you might do in each season. Draw a picture in each box.

Fall	Winter

Spring	Summer

Name _____   Date _____

Hurricanes

Storms can be very scary. A hurricane is a powerful storm. It can cause a lot of damage. Wind and rain can destroy buildings.

The center of a hurricane is called the **eye**. The eye of the storm is very calm.

If you are ever in a hurricane, stay inside. Have flashlights and water with you. Have an adult put boards on your windows so the glass won't break. Talk to your family about what you can do to be safe in a hurricane.

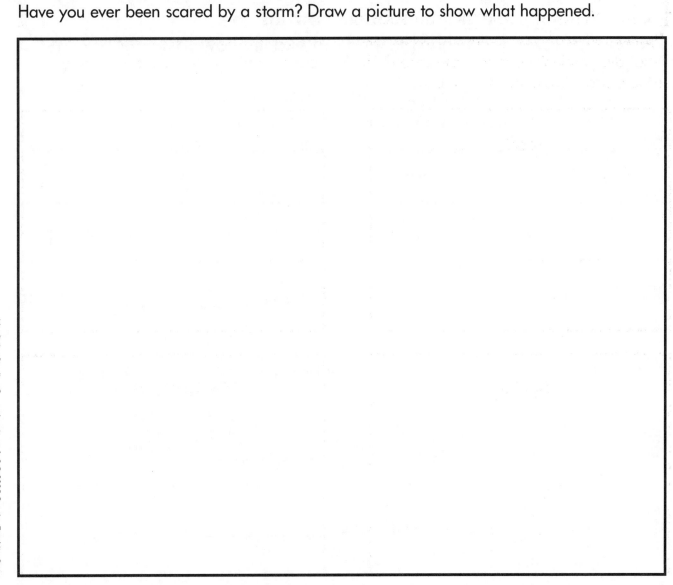

Have you ever been scared by a storm? Draw a picture to show what happened.

Measuring the Weather

How do we know how cold or hot it is outside? How do we know when it is going to rain? Scientists use special instruments to learn about the weather.

A <u>thermometer</u> tells us how cold or hot it is outside. You read a temperature on a thermometer. This can tell you what time of the day is the coldest or hottest.

A <u>barometer</u> tells us if weather is going to change. It may tell us if rain or sunshine is coming.

An <u>anemometer</u> tells us about how fast the wind is blowing. It is hard to find out exactly how fast wind blows.

A weather map tells us what weather is like in different places. It may be a map of a state or a country.

Use the words in the box to complete the sentences.

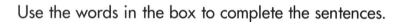

| thermometer | barometer | anemometer | weather map |

1 Is it a good day to fly a kite? I will use an _____ to find out.

2 Is it also cold in another city? I will use a _____ to find out.

3 Will it rain tomorrow? I will use a _____ to find out.

4 How cold is it today? I will use a _____ to find out.

Nonfiction Reading Comprehension • 1–2 © 2005 Creative Teaching Press

Name _____ Date _____

Grand Old Flag

The United States flag is a symbol of America. It has red and white stripes. There are 50 stars on the flag. There is one white star for every state in our country.

Many people believe that Betsy Ross, a seamstress, sewed the first flag in 1776. The story is a legend. No one knows if it is true or false.

People take special care of the flag. It is folded in a special way. The flag is not supposed to touch the ground. This shows respect for our flag.

Look around your town. Where do you see the flag?

The pictures show different words about the flag. Choose a word from the box to match each picture. Write the word on the line under the picture.

| folded | seamstress | sew | stars | stripes |

_____

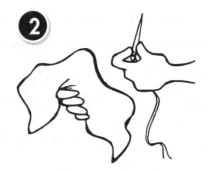

_____

_____

_____

_____

Name _____ Date _____

Liberty Bell

What questions do you have about the Liberty Bell? List them below. Then read the passage to find answers to your questions.

_____

_____

_____

_____

_____

The Liberty Bell is a special part of American history. It rang when America first became a country in 1776. The bell was moved from town to town for Americans to see.

This famous bell has a crack in it. No one knows for sure why the Liberty Bell is cracked. The crack was found when it was rung in 1846. The bell was rung to honor George Washington's birthday. The bell has only been rung a few times since then.

You can still see the Liberty Bell. It is in a special building in Philadelphia, Pennsylvania. It is a symbol of our country's freedom.

Did you find answers to your questions? If not, where could you go to get more information? Talk with your teacher or another adult about how to learn more about the Liberty Bell.

Do You Want to Be a Nurse?

Nurses help people who are sick. They can work in a hospital or a doctor's office. Nurses help doctors. They do a lot themselves, too. They take tests to find out why you are sick. Nurses also give medicine to people so they will feel better.

Nurses work very hard. We need nurses to take care of us.

Do you want to be a nurse when you grow up?

Did a nurse ever take care of you when you were sick? Draw a picture to show what happened.

Name _____ Date _____

Do You Want to Be a Zoologist?

A zoologist is a scientist who studies animals. Zoologists want to learn more about the habits of animals.

Zoologists may study what an animal eats or how it sleeps. They want to help animals stay healthy. Zoologists want to know why animals act the way they do.

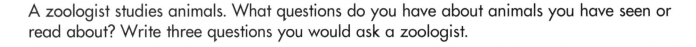

Zoologists may even study humans. We are animals, too!

Do you love animals and science? Maybe you will be a zoologist when you grow up!

A zoologist studies animals. What questions do you have about animals you have seen or read about? Write three questions you would ask a zoologist.

1 _____

_____

2 _____

_____

3 _____

_____

Name _____ Date _____

Do You Want to Be an Architect?

An architect helps people who build homes or buildings. Buildings need to be planned before they are built. Architects draw plans on paper. They may plan a house, school, hospital, or other building. The building may be small. It may also be a tall skyscraper!

Architects may use a computer to help make their plans. They have to meet with the people who will build the building. They talk about the plan to make sure it will work.

Architects are important. They help create buildings in our cities. Do you want to be an architect when you grow up?

What does an architect do?_____

_____

Imagine that you are an architect. What kind of building would you plan? Draw a picture of your plan in the box.

Nonfiction Reading Comprehension • 1–2 © 2005 Creative Teaching Press

Eric Carle

Many children love the book *The Very Hungry Caterpillar*. It was written by Eric Carle. Eric Carle is a famous author who has written many books for children.

Eric Carle was born in New York. He grew up in Germany. He went to school there to be an artist.

When Eric Carle was an adult, he moved back to New York. He had other jobs before he illustrated his first book. Then he started to write and illustrate his own books.

Eric Carle is known today for his beautiful pictures. He uses collage in his books. That means that he takes small pieces of paper and paints them. Then he puts the paper together to make a bigger picture.

Eric Carle lives in Massachusetts. He loves to write books so that he can share stories with kids. His favorite thing to write about is nature.

Eric Carle has given us many wonderful books to enjoy!

What are the important details you learned from the passage? Fill in the blanks.

Who?_____

What?_____

Where?_____

When?_____

Why?_____

Nonfiction Reading Comprehension • 1–2 © 2005 Creative Teaching Press

Name _____ Date _____

Jan Brett

Have you ever read a book by Jan Brett? She has worked on over 25 books. She writes *and* illustrates many of her books. For other books, she only draws the pictures.

When Jan Brett was little, she knew she wanted to write and draw stories. She wrote books as a very young girl.

When Jan was older, she went to school. She would go to museums to look at things. Then she would draw what she saw. She became a very good artist.

Today, Jan loves to travel all around the world. When she visits a new place, it helps her think about ideas for new books.

Do you think you might want to write books one day?

What did you learn about Jan Brett? Complete the graphic organizer. Draw a picture or write a sentence about the beginning, middle, and end of the passage.

Beginning	Middle	End

Name _____ Date _____

The Long Race

How far can you run before you get tired? Do you run fast or slow? Have you ever raced someone else?

Running is a sport that many people enjoy. People run short and long distances. Some people train for a long time to run very far. These athletes run in races called **marathons**.

A marathon is a race that lasts over 26 miles. Runners have to be in very good health to run a marathon. They work hard for many months to be ready for the race.

Runners have to wear special things when they run. Their shoes are very important! They have to run in good shoes. It also helps them to wear clothes that feel light.

One of the most important things all runners must do is drink a lot of water. This helps their body stay cool in a race.

Do you think you could run a marathon someday?

Circle the sentence that tells the main idea of the passage.

1 Runners must drink water.

2 Runners must be very prepared to run a marathon.

3 A marathon is 26 miles.

4 Runners need good shoes.

Nonfiction Reading Comprehension • 1–2 © 2005 Creative Teaching Press

Soccer

Soccer is a very popular game in America. It is also played in many countries all around the world. In some places, soccer is called football.

Boys and girls love to play soccer. The game is played by two teams. Each team tries to kick the soccer ball into the other team's goal.

Most players cannot use their hands or arms during the game. If the ball goes off the field, a player can use his or her hands to throw the ball back into play. The only player who can use his or her hands the entire game is the goalkeeper. This player tries to keep the ball from going into the goal.

The referee watches the players during the game. The referee makes sure that all players are following the rules.

Have you ever played soccer? What else do you know about the sport?

Answer the questions about soccer.

1 What is soccer called in some other places?   _____

2 Which player can use his or her hands during the entire game?   _____

3 Who watches the players during the game to make sure that they are following the rules?   _____

4 How many teams play in one soccer game?   _____

The First Flight

Two brothers invented the airplane. They built the first plane and flew it in 1903. This invention changed the world.

These brothers were named Orville and Wilbur Wright. They made a living fixing bikes! Both brothers were very smart and read a lot. Many people at that time were trying to make an airplane. It was very hard to do. But Orville and Wilbur kept trying for many years. They made many planes that did not work. Then the brothers finally knew they had done it!

Orville and Wilbur flew their plane. The first flight only lasted 12 seconds! Over the years, others used their ideas to make better planes.

Today, we need planes to travel to faraway places. What would our world be like without this invention?

Circle the sentence that tells the main idea of the passage.

1 The first flight only lasted 12 seconds.

2 The Wright brothers worked at a bicycle repair shop.

3 The airplane was an important invention that changed history.

4 The Wright brothers read a lot.

Nonfiction Reading Comprehension • 1–2 © 2005 Creative Teaching Press

Kites

Many people enjoy flying kites. Have you ever wondered when people first started flying kites?

No one knows for sure where or when the first kite was flown in the air. Many people believe that kites were invented over 3,000 years ago in China! One legend says that a farmer in China tied a string to his hat on a windy day and made the first kite. Others think that the first kite was a leaf tied to a string.

Today, kites are fun toys. Adults and kids love to fly kites. They are usually made of a light wood frame. Paper or cloth is used for the main part of the kite. Of course, you need wind to fly your kite, too!

Up, up, and away!

Imagine what a kite might have looked like when it was invented many years ago. Draw a picture of a kite from long ago. Then draw a picture of a kite today.

Long Ago	**Today**

Crayons

When was the last time you colored with crayons? You might have even used crayons today!

Crayons were invented by two cousins in 1903 in New York City. Crayons have been around for over 100 years! The inventors went to visit different schools. They saw that kids needed small, safe crayons to use. They made some out of wax and colored dye. The crayons were a huge hit!

The first crayons came in simple colors, like red, blue, and green. Today, crayons come in many, many different colors. Kids love to color with crayons!

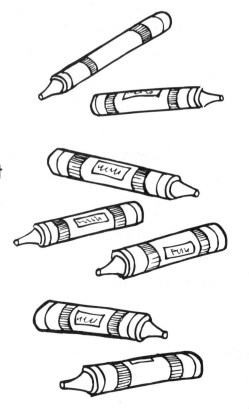

What are the important details you learned from the passage? Fill in the blanks.

Who? _____

What?_____

Where?_____

When?_____

Why?_____

Nonfiction Reading Comprehension • 1–2 © 2005 Creative Teaching Press

Name _____ Date _____

Giant Pandas

The giant panda is a kind of bear. Scientists think that pandas are **solitary** animals. That means they like to be alone.

Giant pandas love to eat bamboo. They eat with flat molars. They can eat 20 to 40 pounds of bamboo in a day! Their habitat, or home, is the forest where bamboo grows.

Giant pandas are found only in China. There are not many pandas alive today. That means they have become an endangered animal. Giant pandas are endangered because they can't find bamboo to eat.

Use context clues to find out what the words mean. Draw a line from each word to its meaning.

1 **solitary**   a small number of an animal is alive

2 **endangered**   teeth

3 **habitat**   alone

4 **molars**   home

Nonfiction Reading Comprehension • 1–2 © 2005 Creative Teaching Press

Name _____ Date _____

Cheetahs

Cheetahs are the fastest mammals on Earth. They can run up to 70 miles an hour. That is as fast as a car may drive on the freeway!

Cheetahs have great eyesight. They can see from very far away. This helps them see animals to eat.

A cheetah also has many spots. The spots help cheetahs hide while they hunt. This is called **camouflage**.

Cheetahs are endangered. Some people worry that cheetahs will become extinct. When an animal is extinct, there are no more alive.

Write facts you read about cheetahs to complete the graphic organizer.

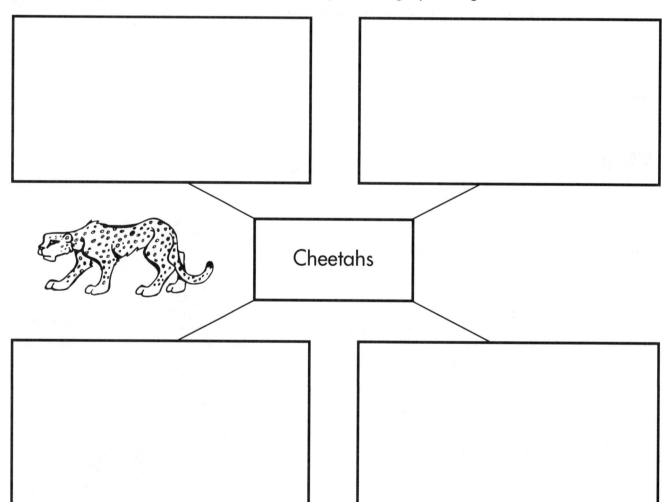

Cheetahs

Nonfiction Reading Comprehension • 1–2 © 2005 Creative Teaching Press

Name _____ Date _____

Sea Turtles

Sea turtles are large turtles. Turtles are reptiles. Reptiles have scaly skin and lay eggs.

Sea turtles lay their eggs on the beach. Females may swim many miles to lay eggs on the same beach where they were born!

Sea turtles live in the warm sea. They are good swimmers and divers. They like to eat crabs, shrimp, and other sea life. Some sea turtles may live to be 80 years old!

Sea turtles are **endangered**. Many people are helping to save the sea turtles. People help protect young turtles so they may live.

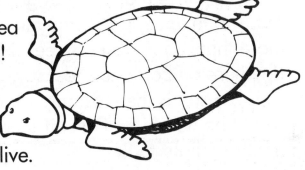

What did you learn about sea turtles? Fill in the blanks.

1 Sea turtles live in the _____.

2 Reptiles have _____ skin.

3 Sea turtles are good _____ and _____.

4 Sea turtles like to eat _____, _____, and other _____.

5 People want to save sea turtles because they are _____.

Nonfiction Reading Comprehension • 1–2 © 2005 Creative Teaching Press

Name _____ Date _____

The Sun

Is the sun a planet or a star? Many people think that the sun is a planet. That is not true. The sun is really a star.

The sun is very big! It is also much closer to Earth than the stars we see at night.

The sun is made of hot gases. It is very, very hot. The temperature in the middle of the sun is more than 25 million degrees. No wonder a sunny day here on Earth can feel so warm!

The sun is the most important part of our solar system. There would be no life on Earth if there were no sun. We need the sun's heat and light to live.

Find the words about the sun in the word search.

Earth	heat	hot	solar system	star	sun

S O L A R S Y S T E M

A S T Y S U N V K L J

G I T R P M R N E C S

D A L A X D O L Y H T

L C A P P D E N C O A

U L I M O P H E A T R

E A R T H L I E R H L

Nonfiction Reading Comprehension • 1–2 © 2005 Creative Teaching Press

Saturn

There are many interesting facts to learn about Saturn.

Saturn is the sixth planet from the sun. It has rings around it. The rings are made of ice and rock. You need a telescope to see the rings from Earth.

Earth has one moon, but Saturn has many moons. Some have names, like Atlas and Titan.

Saturn is the second-largest planet in the solar system. If Saturn were hollow, 764 Earths would fit inside it!

Write details you learned about Saturn to complete the graphic organizer.

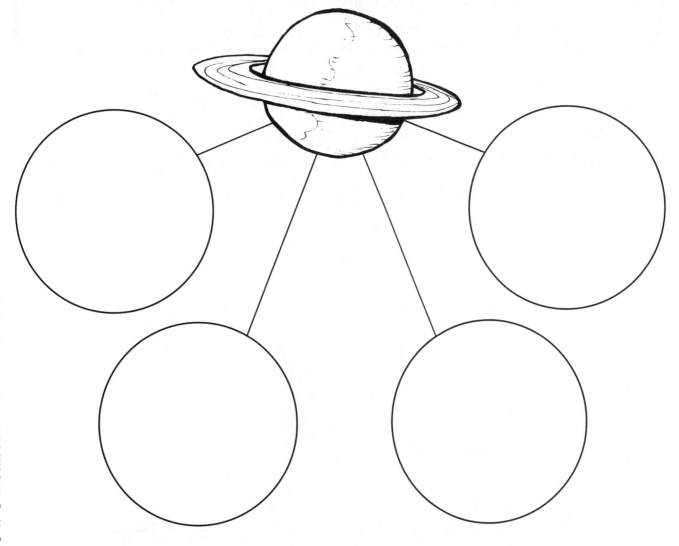

Asteroids and Comets

What is out in space? A sun, moons, and other planets are all in space. There are also asteroids and comets in space!

Asteroids are made of rock and metal. They orbit, or go around, the sun. Small asteroids are the size of a pebble. Asteroids can also be very, very large.

Comets are made of gas and ice. They also orbit the sun. Comets have a head and a tail.

When you look up at the night sky, think about comets and asteroids. They are out in space, too.

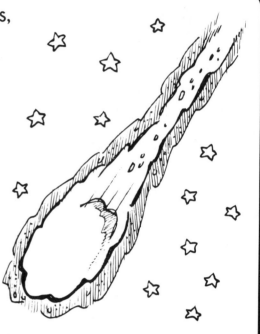

What do asteroids and comets have in common? How are they different? Use the facts listed below to complete the Venn diagram.

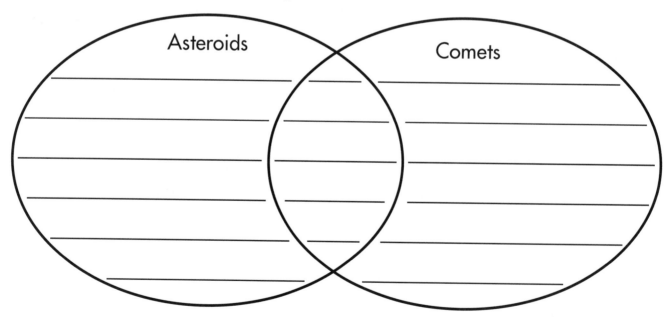

- made of gas and ice
- orbit the sun
- have a head and a tail

- made of rock and metal
- in space
- can be small or large

Nonfiction Reading Comprehension • 1–2 © 2005 Creative Teaching Press

Name _____ Date _____

Ocean Life

There are five oceans on Earth. These oceans are home to some of the most interesting creatures! Scientists think more than 1 million creatures live in the ocean.

In parts of the ocean, the water is very cold. In other parts, it is very warm. Animals live in water that is just right for them.

Many animals in the ocean eat other ocean animals. Ocean animals have to make sure that they are not eaten by their predators. They do this in a few ways. Some fish, like the stonefish, are poisonous. Other animals, like the stingray, sting their predators. Some animals, like a rock bass, are the same color as the plants in the water so they are hard to spot. There is even one fish that has a spot on its tail that looks like an eye. That way, a predator thinks it is in front of the fish instead of behind it!

Read each sentence. Write **T** if the sentence is true or **F** if it is false.

1 _____ There are more than 1 million animals in the ocean.

2 _____ Animals in the ocean only eat seaweed.

3 _____ Animals in the ocean have to protect themselves from other animals.

4 _____ All ocean water is very cold.

5 _____ Some fish sting their predators.

6 _____ There are seven oceans on Earth.

Tide Pools

What is a tide? Tides are caused by a pull between Earth and the moon. When it is high tide, the ocean swells and there is more water on the shore. When it is low tide, ocean water rolls farther away from the shore.

Tide pools form in low tide. Tide pools are small pools of water left along the shore. Many plants and animals live in tide pools. Sea stars, kelp, and crabs are some of the living creatures you might see in a tide pool.

The plants and animals in tide pools have to be able to live in both wet and dry places. They also have to be used to being cold and warm. Hard waves can also hurt animals in the tide pools. A tide pool is a tough place to live!

Circle the sentence that tells the main idea of the passage.

1 Tide pools are wet and dry.

2 Tide pools are home to plants and animals that must be able to survive many changes.

3 Tide pools form along the shoreline during low tide.

4 Sea stars live in tide pools.

5 Waves can crash into tide pools.

Nonfiction Reading Comprehension • 1–2 © 2005 Creative Teaching Press

Name _____ Date _____

Pollution

The ocean is home to many living things. Yet, there are big problems with keeping the ocean clean.

How does the ocean become polluted? Oil spills are serious. Big ships spill oil that harms plants and animals. Trash is dumped in the water, too. Trash, such as a plastic bag, can trap an animal and hurt it. Some animals may also mistake trash for food, eat it, and get sick or die.

Many scientists want people to take better care of our oceans. Pollution harms both the water and all the plants and animals that live there.

How can you do your part? One way is to never litter or throw garbage on the ground or on a beach.

People around the world can help keep the oceans clean.

Think about other ways that you can help keep the oceans clean. Draw a picture in the box.

Nonfiction Reading Comprehension • 1–2 © 2005 Creative Teaching Press

George Washington

George Washington was the first President of the United States. He was a strong leader. He helped to set up our country. He had a great vision for how our country should be. George Washington did not live in the White House. The White House had not been built when he was in office.

We take time to remember George Washington around his birthday in February. Our country celebrates Presidents' Day in honor of Washington and Abraham Lincoln.

Read each sentence. Circle the word or words that make the sentence true.

1 George Washington did not _____.
   live in the White House
   have a Vice President

2 Presidents' Day honors both George Washington and _____.
   Abraham Lincoln
   John Adams

3 George Washington was the first _____.
   person to come to America
   President of the United States

4 George Washington was a _____.
   quiet man
   strong leader

5 George Washington's birthday is in _____.
   May
   February

Nonfiction Reading Comprehension • 1–2 © 2005 Creative Teaching Press

Name _____ Date _____

Dr. Seuss

What do you know about Dr. Seuss? What do you want to know? Fill in the first two columns of the KWL chart before you read the passage.

Reading is one of the best things that a child can do. Many children want something fun to read. Books by Dr. Seuss are very fun to read!

Dr. Seuss is one of the most famous authors of all time. Dr. Seuss was born Theodor Seuss Geisel. When he was young, he liked to draw pictures. When he grew up, he decided to write books for children. He wanted children to have good books to read.

Dr. Seuss wrote 54 books. Most of them were written for children. One of his most famous books is *The Cat in the Hat*. Many, many children have grown up reading his books!

What books have you read by Dr. Seuss?

Now that you've read about Dr. Seuss, fill in the last column of the KWL chart.

What You **K**now	What You **W**ant to Know	What You **L**earned

Name _____ Date _____

Jackie Robinson

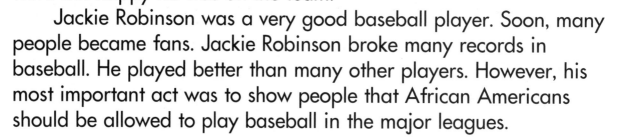

Jackie Robinson was a famous baseball player. Why was he famous? He was the first African American to play baseball in the major leagues. The major leagues are for the best baseball players.

Jackie Robinson loved to play sports his entire life. As he grew older, he played sports in school. African Americans did not play baseball in the major leagues at that time. Jackie began to play for the Brooklyn Dodgers in 1947. Many people were not happy he was on the team.

Jackie Robinson was a very good baseball player. Soon, many people became fans. Jackie Robinson broke many records in baseball. He played better than many other players. However, his most important act was to show people that African Americans should be allowed to play baseball in the major leagues.

What are the important details you learned from the passage? Fill in the blanks.

Who? _____

What?_____

Where?_____

When?_____

Why?_____

Nonfiction Reading Comprehension • 1–2 © 2005 Creative Teaching Press

Name _____ Date _____

Sally Ride

What is it like to travel into space? Just ask Sally Ride. Sally Ride was the first American woman in space.

Sally wanted to be a tennis player when she was young. She was very good at tennis. When she was older, Sally decided to stop playing tennis. She wanted to train to be an astronaut. Sally was chosen out of 8,000 other people. She learned to be an astronaut.

In 1983, Sally Ride went into space. Today, she helps girls do well in science and math. She wants more women to travel into space.

This passage tells about Sally Ride's life in the order events happened. Fill in the blanks.

When she was young, Sally _____

_____.

When she was older, Sally wanted to _____

_____.

In 1983, Sally_____

_____.

Today, Sally _____

_____.

Name _____   Date _____

Deserts

Deserts are usually very hot. But people don't always know that deserts can get very cold, too. It can even snow in a desert!

It does not rain very much in most deserts. Yet many plants and animals live in the desert. Why?

Desert plants and animals can survive with little water. Some animals in the desert sleep during the day. They only come out at night when it is cool. These animals are called **nocturnal** animals. Desert plants, like the cactus, can store water to stay alive.

The largest desert is in Africa. We have deserts in the United States, too.

What details did you learn about the desert? Fill in the web.

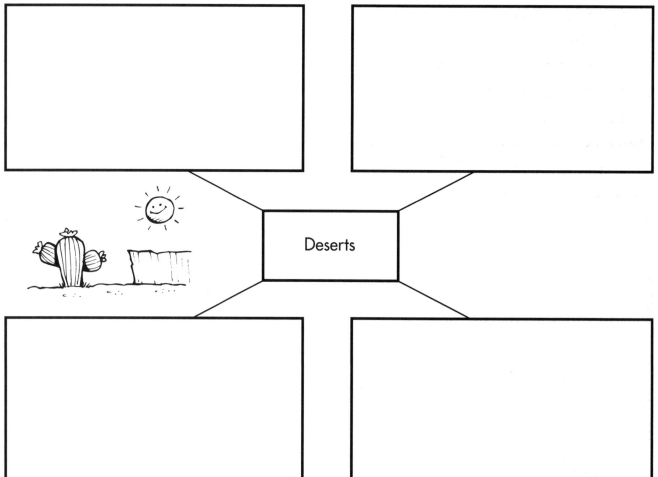

Deserts

Nonfiction Reading Comprehension • 1–2 © 2005 Creative Teaching Press

Name _____ Date _____

Rain Forests

Rain forests are wet and warm forests. It never gets very cold or very hot in the rain forest. Most rain forests are very green.

There are many plants and animals that live in the rain forest. They usually live in one part of the forest. It might be high in the trees or on the floor of the forest.

The howler monkey lives in the rain forest. It gets its name from the loud howls it makes. It is the loudest animal on land. The howler monkey can be heard from 3 miles away!

The rain forests of the world are in trouble. Many people cut down the trees in the rain forests. This hurts the plants and animals that live there. Groups are working hard to save the rain forests. What can you do to help save the rain forest?

Draw a picture that shows what you might be able to do to help save the rain forests.

Nonfiction Reading Comprehension • 1–2 © 2005 Creative Teaching Press

Grasslands

When you can look out and see grass for miles and miles, you just might be in a grassland! Grasslands can be found on every continent except for Antarctica. In some places, the grasslands are called prairies.

The <u>climate</u> in the grasslands around the world can be hot or cold. Some grasslands that are close to the equator are hot all year. Others, such as the prairies in the United States, have <u>frigid</u> winters and hot summers.

The grasslands are home to many animals. Animals that love to <u>graze</u> on grass are especially <u>content</u>. Bison are animals that live on the American prairie. They live in <u>herds</u> that are anywhere from one family to thousands of bison.

Many different plants also grow in the grasslands. Beautiful flowers bloom in the prairie, too.

There is so much life on the prairie!

Look at the underlined words. What do they mean? Use context clues to help you write their meanings.

1 climate _____

2 frigid _____

3 graze _____

4 content _____

5 herds _____

Nonfiction Reading Comprehension • 1–2 © 2005 Creative Teaching Press

Name _____ Date _____

Tundra

What do you know about the tundra? What do you want to know? Fill in the first two columns of the KWL chart before you read the passage.

> Think about a time when you were very, very cold. You might have been outside on a snowy day. Or the weather may have changed one day and you did not have a warm jacket.
>
> The tundra is colder than anywhere else on Earth. The tundra is found at the top of the world! It is near the North Pole.
>
> The tundra has very little rain. However, the freezing temperatures make the ground frozen almost all year long. That means the tundra has very little water.
>
> How does any plant or animal live in the tundra? Animals have to learn to live in the cold. Plants bloom during the very short summer.
>
> The tundra is a very cool place!

Now that you've read about the tundra, fill in the last column of the KWL chart.

What You **K**now	What You **W**ant to Know	What You **L**earned

Nonfiction Reading Comprehension • 1–2 © 2005 Creative Teaching Press

The White House

The White House is the place where our president lives. It is located in Washington, D.C. It is over 200 years old.

The White House is a very large home. It has 132 rooms and 35 bathrooms! There is also a swimming pool and a movie theater at the White House.

The White House is where our president works, too. His office is called the Oval Office. This is because the room is in the shape of an oval.

The White House has an amazing history. There have been two fires at the White House. Many important leaders from around the world have visited the White House. The White House has also had a few different names before becoming the White House in 1901. One name was the "President's House."

This American landmark is one of a kind.

Read each sentence. Fill in the bubble next to the word or words that make the sentence true.

1. The White House has also been known as the _____.
   ○ President's House   ○ Black House   ○ American House

2. The White House is in _____.
   ○ Washington, D.C.   ○ New York   ○ San Francisco

3. The president's office is called the _____.
   ○ President's Office   ○ White Office   ○ Oval Office

4. The White House has _____ rooms.
   ○ 102   ○ 35   ○ 132

5. There have been _____ fires at the White House.
   ○ 5   ○ 2   ○ 6

Nonfiction Reading Comprehension • 1–2 © 2005 Creative Teaching Press

Name _____ Date _____

Mount Rushmore

Mount Rushmore is a special American landmark. It is a famous <u>sculpture</u> in South Dakota. Many people visit it each day.

It took 14 years to <u>carve</u> the four faces on Mount Rushmore. It was finished in 1941.

The landmark shows four important American presidents. George Washington, Thomas Jefferson, Theodore Roosevelt, and Abraham Lincoln are all on Mount Rushmore. Each man helped our country in many ways.

Mount Rushmore is <u>enormous</u>. Each face is 60 feet high!

This landmark is a very special <u>tribute</u> to four presidents and what they did for America.

Use context clues to find out what the words mean. Draw a line from each word to its meaning

1 **sculpture**   very large

2 **carve**   statue or monument

3 **enormous**   honor or compliment

4 **tribute**   shape into an object

The Golden Gate Bridge

The Golden Gate Bridge in San Francisco, California, is one of the most famous landmarks in America. People from all over the world come to take pictures of the famous bridge.

The bridge was built in four years. It was finished in 1937. Before it was built, people had to take boats to get over to San Francisco.

The Golden Gate Bridge is not golden. It is orange. It is named for the entrance from the Pacific Ocean into the San Francisco bay.

More than 1 billion cars have crossed the bridge since it opened. Many people now walk or ride a bike over the bridge each day. The Golden Gate Bridge sure is a popular landmark!

These pictures show the history of the Golden Gate Bridge. What is the correct order? Number the pictures from 1 to 4.

Listen to the Orchestra!

Strike up the band! But what instruments do you hear?

It can be hard to tell which instrument is making each sound. If you go to the orchestra, you will hear four types of instruments.

Most of the instruments in the orchestra are called <u>string</u> instruments. They are given this name because they have strings. People play the strings with their hands or with a bow. A violin is one string instrument.

Some of the sounds in an orchestra come from <u>woodwind</u> instruments. Most of these instruments are made of wood. They need "wind" to make a sound. The wind comes from the player's breath. A clarinet is a woodwind instrument.

What about those loud horns? These are part of the <u>brass</u> family. The tuba is a member of this family. These instruments are made of brass or other metal. They have longs tubes that make sounds.

Don't forget the drums! An orchestra always has drums. They are part of the <u>percussion</u> family. People hit, scrape, or shake things to make noise. They help keep the beat for the rest of the band. You can usually hear the drums or cymbals.

People who play music are called musicians. They practice very hard to play well. Once someone plays for an orchestra, he or she has probably played the instrument for many years.

Do you have a band at your school? Maybe you will learn to play an instrument. You might play in an orchestra one day.

Nonfiction Reading Comprehension • 1–2 © 2005 Creative Teaching Press

Family of Instruments

What did you learn about each family of instruments? Write one or more facts below.

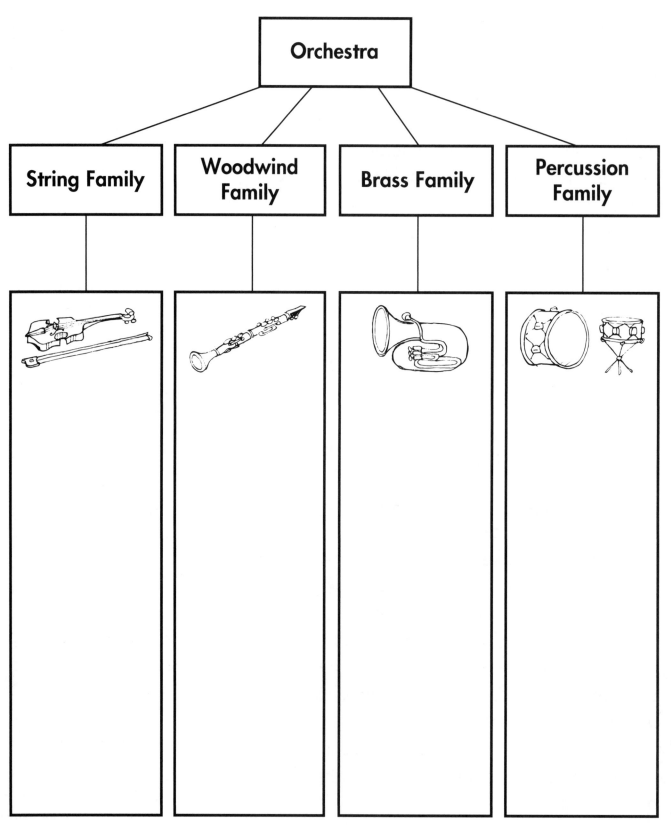

Nonfiction Reading Comprehension • 1–2 © 2005 Creative Teaching Press

Name _____ Date _____

Orchestra Vocabulary

Find these vocabulary words in the word search.

brass	drum	horn	instrument
orchestra	practice	sound	string
tuba	woodwind	cymbal	music

```
I   B   R   A   S   S   S   C   O   U   T
N   E   L   F   W   F   Y   T   O   U
S   Y   M   B   O   L   M   O   R   H
T   S   H   P   O   A   B   C   C   P
R   O   A   R   D   T   A   I   H   S
U   U   T   A   W   R   L   L   E   T
M   N   H   C   I   T   U   U   S   R
E   D   O   T   N   B   U   M   T   I
N   I   R   I   D   A   H   B   R   N
T   V   N   C   T   B   E   Y   A   G
P   R   T   E   A   M   U   S   I   C
```

Getting Around

How did you get to school today? Maybe you took a bus. You might have gone to school in a car. Did you ride your bike?

There are many different ways to get around. We see cars and trucks on our roads every day. We can even ride a bike or scooter around town! Airplanes take us to places that are farther away.

How did people get around before cars, trucks, and planes? One way was to go by horse. People rode horses to get from place to place. Horses also pulled wagons or carts to help move things.

Covered wagons were used when people moved long distances. These wagons were very heavy. Six to eight horses had to work together to pull the wagon. A short trip could take a long time.

Bikes also came along in the 1800s. The first bikes were like the ones we have today, except there were no pedals! A rider had to move the bike forward with his or her feet.

Trains were another way that people got around in the past. Trains took people long distances. It was much nicer to ride a train than to ride a horse!

Cars were invented in the early 1900s. This was a very exciting change! Many people bought a car and drove to get from place to place. This made trips much faster.

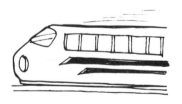

Today, we have so many ways to get around quickly. Humans can even travel into space on a space shuttle!

Transportation sure has changed since the past. Think of all the ways that you get around today.

Nonfiction Reading Comprehension • 1–2 © 2005 Creative Teaching Press

Traveling

Is it easier or harder to travel today? Complete the sentences.

1 In the past, I might have used _____ to get around.

2 This would have been hard because _____

_____

_____ .

3 This would have been easy because _____

_____

_____ .

4 Today, I use _____ to get around.

5 This is hard because _____

_____

_____ .

6 This is easy because _____

_____

_____ .

Name _____ Date _____

Transportation Changes

Think about ways that transportation has changed. Fill in the chart with facts.

Transportation in the Past	Transportation Today

Nonfiction Reading Comprehension • 1–2 © 2005 Creative Teaching Press

Christopher Columbus

Christopher Columbus was a brave explorer and sailor. He helped change the history of the world!

Columbus was born in Italy in 1451. At that time, countries were trading items with each other. Spices, gold, and silk were some of the things that were traded abetween countries.

Columbus was curious about new places for trading. The King and Queen of Spain gave him money to sail. In 1492, he set off to cross the Atlantic Ocean. No one had tried to cross the ocean before. Columbus sailed with many other people. They had three ships.

People were very worried about Columbus. Many did not think he would make it to land. They thought that crossing the ocean was very dangerous.

Christopher Columbus sailed for three months. When he saw land, he did not know where he was. He had landed to the south of where the United States is today.

People called this place the "New World." That is because this part of the world was new to everyone. No one had ever been there before.

After this trip, Columbus went back to the New World three more times. Each time he found more land and learned something about this new place.

Christopher Columbus helped others understand that there was a lot more to learn about the world. Many other explorers set out for new places after Columbus. These brave sailors shaped the history of the world!

Columbus Timeline

The passage is written in the order in which events happened. Can you make a timeline of Christopher Columbus's life? Add 3 events to the timeline.

1451 —

_____
_____
_____
_____

1492 —

_____
_____
_____
_____

_____
_____
_____
_____

Nonfiction Reading Comprehension • 1–2 © 2005 Creative Teaching Press

Columbus Main Idea

1 Which sentence tells the main idea about the passage you read about Christopher Columbus? Circle the main idea.

The King and Queen of Spain sent Christopher Columbus to find new places for trading.

Christopher Columbus was a brave sailor who discovered a new world.

Christopher Columbus was born in Italy.

Countries traded spice, gold, and other objects.

Christopher Columbus sailed for three months during his first trip.

2 Write three details you read in the passage.

_____

_____

_____

_____

Fossils

If you have ever heard of fossils, you might just think of dinosaur bones. Sure, old dinosaur bones are fossils. But fossils can be other things, too.

A fossil is any proof of something that was alive in the past. It can be proof of a plant or an animal. It doesn't have to be part of the actual living thing. It can be an animal's footprint.

Many fossils are the hard parts of animals or plants, like a shell or teeth. This is because hard body parts, like bones, survive longer than soft body parts.

What happens to a fossil over thousands of years? An animal or a plant dies. Part of the dead animal or plant is buried. Then it hardens and becomes a rock. Most fossils are rocks that have been made by layers of sand, mud, and clay.

Scientists are always looking for fossils. These scientists are called **paleontologists**. Paleontologists go out to places to find fossils. They often have to dig a lot to find a fossil. When they find one, they collect it very carefully.

Paleontologists also make sure to wash and care for the fossil. They try to figure out what kind of animal or plant they have found. Scientists also want to know how old the fossil is.

But scientists are not the only people who find fossils. You can even find them—if you know where to look! Fossils can be found on every continent on Earth.

Do you think you have any fossils in your town? Why don't you try looking for one!

Nonfiction Reading Comprehension • 1–2 © 2005 Creative Teaching Press

Fossils Graphic Organizer

What facts did you learn about fossils? Fill in the graphic organizer.

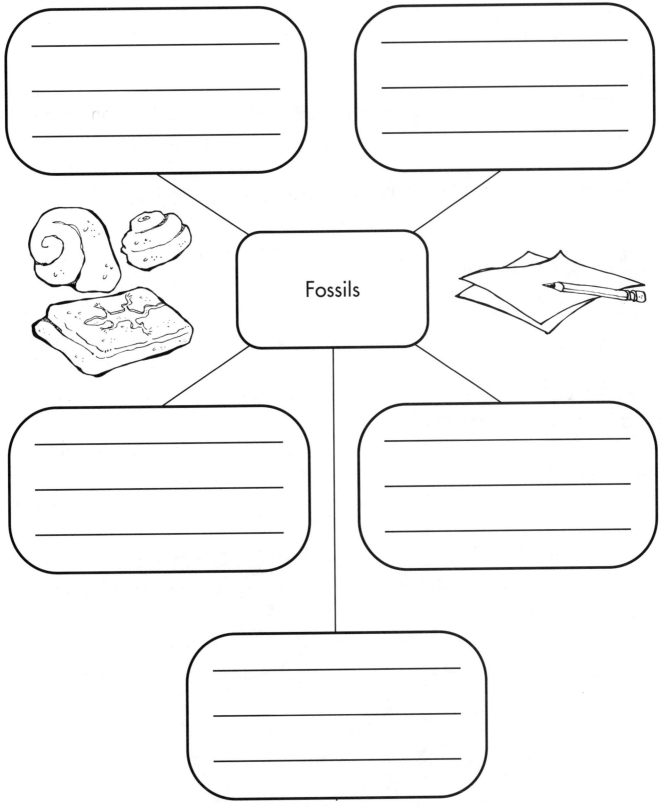

What Happens to Fossils?

You read about what happens to a fossil over time. Put the following events in the correct order. Number them from 1 to 7.

___ Part of the plant or animal is buried.

___ Once the fossil is found, it is washed and identified.

___ The plant or animal hardens over time and becomes a rock.

___ A plant or an animal dies.

___ After scientists know what the fossil is, they try to find out how old it is.

___ Scientists discover the fossil.

___ Scientists dig for fossils.

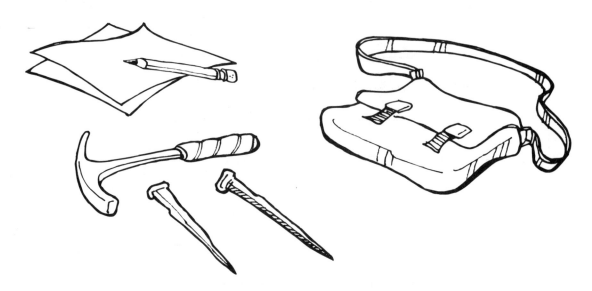

Nonfiction Reading Comprehension • 1–2 © 2005 Creative Teaching Press

Growing a Garden

Growing plants in a garden can be a lot of fun! But it can also be a lot of work. What does it take to grow plants in a garden? Here is what you would need:

- All plants need sun to grow. Some plants need more sun than others. If your garden gets a lot of sun, you will need plants that love sun. If your garden is in the shade, there are plants that like shade, too.

- Good soil helps plants grow. Some soil has too much clay in it. Other soil has too much sand in it. Find the soil that is right for your plants.

- You need plants for your garden! Remember that plants grow well at different times of the year. Make sure to plant things at the right time. When you plant the garden, leave space between your plants. This is so the roots of the plants can grow and are not crowded.

- Once your garden is planted, you have to keep the plants alive! Make sure to water the plants when they are dry. It is a good idea to water in the morning so the sun can dry off any extra water.

- When you grow plants, you will probably have weeds. Weeds are any plant that you do not want to grow in your garden. Weeds sometimes look like pretty plants. However, they "take" the water from the plants you want to grow. Pulling weeds is part of taking care of your garden.

- If you need help with your garden, there are many places to go. A store that sells plants can help you learn what to grow in a garden. Also, checking out a book about plants from the library can teach you how to take care of your garden.

Nonfiction Reading Comprehension • 1–2 © 2005 Creative Teaching Press

Name _____ Date _____

Taking Care of a Garden

List the five things you need to do to take care of a garden.

1 _____

_____

2 _____

_____

3 _____

_____

4 _____

_____

5 _____

_____

Nonfiction Reading Comprehension • 1–2 © 2005 Creative Teaching Press

Working in a Garden

Look at the pictures. They show someone working in the garden. What happens because of each of these actions? Draw a picture to show the result.

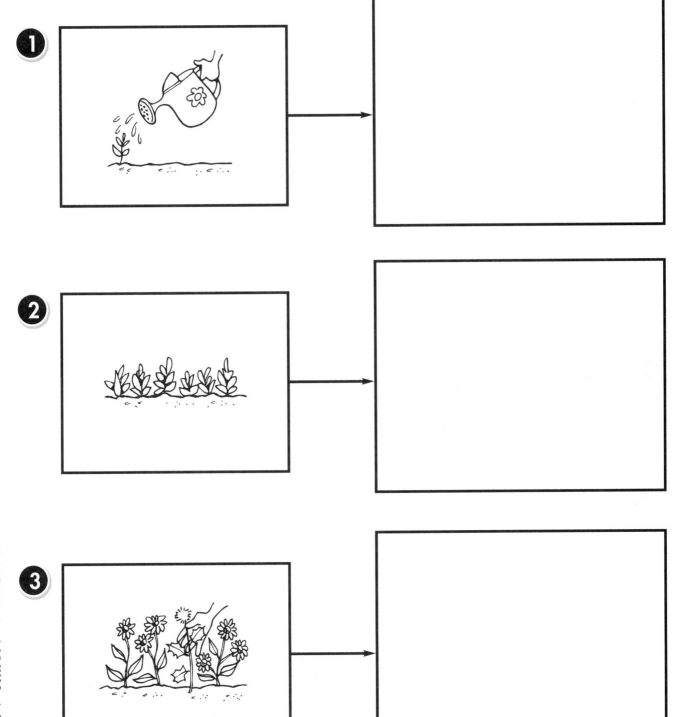

Name _____ Date _____

Earth Day

Planet Earth needs our help. All people must work together to protect Earth and keep it clean. We now have a special holiday every year to celebrate our planet. It is called Earth Day.

Earth Day is a holiday that is celebrated around the world. It started many years ago. People were worried about pollution. They wanted to make sure that others knew how important it was to keep the planet clean. They thought that making a holiday might help others learn about this.

They were right. Since Earth Day has started, people are much more aware of how to keep Earth clean. New laws protect our water and air. More people reuse and recycle. Parks and beaches are cleaner. There is land set aside for animals to live.

Earth Day happens in April each year. But you can celebrate Earth Day all year round! How can you take care of Earth each day? Here are some ideas:

- Don't throw trash on the ground.
- Plant a tree.
- Help clean up a park or school in your town.
- Recycle paper, bottles, and cans.
- Don't waste water.
  (Turn off the water when you brush your teeth.)
- Walk instead of driving in a car.

Can you think of any other ideas? Share them with your friends and family.

_____

_____

_____

Taking Care of Our Planet

Think about what might happen if people did not take care of the planet. Draw a picture to show your thinking.

Nonfiction Reading Comprehension • 1–2 © 2005 Creative Teaching Press

Planet Problems

How do people around you help take care of the planet? Write about one problem in your school or your town. Explain how you would fix the problem.

_____

_____

_____

_____

_____

_____

_____

_____

_____

_____

_____

Nonfiction Reading Comprehension • 1–2 © 2005 Creative Teaching Press

Volcanoes

Go outside and look at the ground. What do you think is far below the ground?

Remember that the earth's surface can be miles and miles above the center of the earth. What is the center of the earth like?

Under the ground we walk on, the planet has many layers. Some of these layers are hard, while others are not.

There are parts of the inside of the earth that are very hot. This heat turns rock into liquid. The hot liquid rock rises up to the earth's surface. This is how a volcano erupts. A volcano is a way that the planet cools itself.

What is inside a volcano? Most volcanoes are made of lava and ash. Lava is the hot liquid rock that flows from a volcano.

There are many volcanoes all around the world. Some volcanoes will not erupt again. These volcanoes are <u>extinct</u>. Others have not erupted for thousands of years, but they could erupt again. These are called <u>dormant</u> volcanoes. <u>Active</u> volcanoes are volcanoes that people watch and think will erupt someday. Some active volcanoes even erupt every day!

There are scientists who study volcanoes. They are called geologists. They watch volcanoes and look for any activity. The eruption of a volcano can be hard to predict.

Many volcanoes are under water and we cannot even see them. The United States has many volcanoes. They are found in the western part of our country. Hawaii and Alaska have many volcanoes.

Go outside and look at the ground again. Think about the planet's layers and the power of a volcano!

Comparing Volcanoes

The passage you read compares three kinds of volcanoes. Describe each kind of volcano.

Extinct Volcano	Dormant Volcano	Active Volcano
_____	_____	_____
_____	_____	_____
_____	_____	_____
_____	_____	_____
_____	_____	_____
_____	_____	_____
_____	_____	_____
_____	_____	_____
_____	_____	_____
_____	_____	_____
_____	_____	_____
_____	_____	_____

Nonfiction Reading Comprehension • 1–2 © 2005 Creative Teaching Press

Name _____ Date _____

Volcano Crossword

Fill in the crossword puzzle. Use words you learned from the passage about volcanoes.

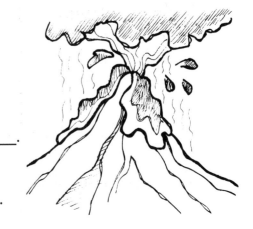

Across
1. Underground, the earth has many _____.
5. Hot liquid rock is called _____.
6. We can't see volcanoes that are under _____.

Down
2. Scientists who study volcanoes are called _____.
3. Volcanoes are made of lava and _____.
4. The state of _____ has many volcanoes.
7. It is hard to predict when a volcano may _____.

Computer Safety

Computers are an important part of our world. You have probably seen or used one yourself.

There are many things that you can do with a computer. You can find a lot of information on the computer. You can use e-mail to send messages to other people. You can use a computer to type a story or letter. You can even make pictures or other kinds of art. Computer games are fun, too!

There are rules that you should follow when you use a computer. One rule is that computers need to be treated carefully of so they don't break. This means that eating and drinking near a computer is a bad idea. Also, hitting or slamming the keys on the keyboard can harm the computer.

Also, it is important to sit in front of the computer the right way. Just as you wear a helmet when you ride your bike, using a computer the correct way helps protect your body. This means sitting up straight, with your feet on the floor. Your eyes should be at the same level as the words on the screen.

Many kids who use computers go on the Internet. The Internet allows your computer to "talk" to other computers. This is how you can use e-mail and visit Web sites. But you need to be safe when you are on the Internet.

One good rule to follow is to never give anyone your name, address, or phone number on the computer. Check with an adult before you send a picture of yourself to someone. It is smart to keep your password a secret, too.

Now that you know the rules, have fun!

Nonfiction Reading Comprehension • 1–2 © 2005 Creative Teaching Press

Name _____ Date _____

Computer Rules

List the most important computer rules that you learned from the passage.

1 _____

_____

2 _____

_____

3 _____

_____

4 _____

_____

5 _____

_____

Nonfiction Reading Comprehension • 1–2 © 2005 Creative Teaching Press

Name _____ Date _____

Is It True?

Read each sentence. Write **T** if the sentence is true or **F** if it is false.

1 ____ You can use computers for many things.

2 ____ Eating while you work on the computer is a good idea.

3 ____ You must give your phone number to anyone who sends you an e-mail.

4 ____ Sitting up straight in front of the computer can help protect your body.

5 ____ The words on the screen should be below the level of your eyes.

6 ____ Give your password to your teacher only.

7 ____ Hitting the keyboard can help fix a broken computer.

8 ____ Keep your feet flat on the floor when you work on the computer.

Nonfiction Reading Comprehension • 1–2 © 2005 Creative Teaching Press

The Great Wall of China

Can you imagine building a wall around your school? What about a wall around your city? Think about putting a wall around your state. How long would it be? How many people would work together to finish it?

There is one wall in this world that is amazing. The Great Wall of China is over 2,000 years old! It is the longest <u>structure</u> ever built. It is 4,000 miles long. The Great Wall of China is long enough to <u>span</u> the entire United States and still have 1,000 miles left!

The wall was built to protect people in China from <u>invaders</u>. It was also built between areas of the country that fought with each other.

Many people worked very hard to build the wall. It took over 200 years to finish. Some people died from their hard work. One <u>legend</u> says that some men are still buried in the wall.

Different <u>emperors</u>, or leaders, wanted the wall to be finished. Some people think that almost 1 million workers helped finish the wall. That sure is a lot of work!

The Great Wall of China is so long that it can be seen from space. <u>Astronauts</u> have taken pictures of the wall while <u>orbiting</u> Earth.

Today, the wall does not protect China from others. But it is a very special place. It will never be taken down.

Many people from around the world travel to China to see this great <u>landmark.</u> It is unlike anything else in the world.

What Do You Want to Know?

What questions do you have about the Great Wall of China? List them below. Then read the passage to find answers to your questions.

You might not find all your answers in the passage. Where could you go to get more information? Talk with your teacher or another adult about how to learn more about the Great Wall of China.

_____

_____

_____

_____

_____

_____

_____

_____

_____

Nonfiction Reading Comprehension • 1–2 © 2005 Creative Teaching Press

What Does It Mean?

Use context clues to find out what the words mean. Draw a line from each word to its meaning.

1 span   travelers in a spacecraft

2 invaders   revolving around

3 legend   story that may or may not be true

4 emperors   something built

5 orbiting   special place

6 landmark   extend across

7 astronauts   leaders

8 structure   people who want to attack

Yellowstone National Park

Yellowstone is one of America's most beautiful parks. It is in Wyoming. Many people travel each year to spend some time there.

You would see many animals if you went to visit Yellowstone. One animal you would see is the <u>bison</u>, the largest mammal in Yellowstone. People in America often call them buffalo.

Another animal that you could see in Yellowstone is a bear. Black bears and grizzly bears live in Yellowstone Park. You might even see <u>cubs</u> with their mother. Never give human food to bears. When they eat our food, bears stop hunting for themselves. They can be very mean if they are hungry and smell food.

Gray wolves also live in Yellowstone. You usually see wolves in a <u>pack</u>. This means that they travel in groups, like a family. These wolves were once <u>endangered</u>. Many people are working to keep them alive.

Have you ever seen an otter riding a waterfall? Well, you might see that in Yellowstone. River otters live there. The otters live in the water in summer and winter. Their thick fur helps them to <u>survive</u> the cold winter.

One of the most famous sights in Yellowstone is called Old Faithful. What is it? Old Faithful is a <u>geyser</u>. A geyser is water that is pushed into the air. It is caused by water that is heated underground. The water becomes <u>steam</u>, or gas. Then the steam pushes other water into the air. There are more geysers in Yellowstone than anywhere else in the world.

There sure are many interesting sights in Yellowstone!

Nonfiction Reading Comprehension • 1–2 © 2005 Creative Teaching Press

Word Meaning

What do the following words mean? Look at context clues in the passage to help you. Write the meaning of each word.

1 pack _____

2 endangered _____

3 steam _____

4 geyser _____

5 cubs _____

6 bison _____

7 survive _____

Name _____ Date _____

Yellowstone Sentences

Read the six words in the word box. These are words from the passage. Write each word in a sentence.

pack	endangered	steam	geyser	cubs	bison

1 _____

_____

2 _____

_____

3 _____

_____

4 _____

_____

5 _____

_____

6 _____

_____

Nonfiction Reading Comprehension • 1–2 © 2005 Creative Teaching Press

Bread Around the World

Do you eat bread? Maybe you even had a piece of bread for breakfast or lunch today!

People all around the world eat bread. However, bread found in other countries might be different than what you eat here in America.

All bread is made of flour. Flour is made from different kinds of grains.

Americans eat many kinds of bread. Some people eat bread when they have a sandwich. We also eat small rolls of bread. Hot dog and hamburger buns are bread, too!

In Mexico, many people eat <u>tortillas</u>. A tortilla is a thin, flat kind of bread. Sometimes people put food in the tortilla and wrap it up into a taco or burrito.

In Israel, many people eat <u>pita bread</u>. A tortilla is a kind of bread that has a "pocket" in which people can put all different kinds of fillings.

In Italy, many people eat <u>pizza</u>. Pizza is a kind of bread with tomato sauce, cheese, or other food on top. Pizza is a popular food in many countries!

In France, many people eat long loaves of bread. They are called <u>baguettes</u>. The bread might be eaten with cheese or by itself.

There are so many wonderful kinds of bread to eat. The good news is that you don't have to travel the world to try different breads. Many of these breads can be found right here in the United States. Many cities have restaurants with food from other countries. What kinds of bread can you eat in your town?

Are you hungry for bread? Which kind of bread?

Name _____ Date _____

Bread

Fill in the blanks to complete the chart. Write **yes** or **no** in the last column to specify if you have eaten that type of bread.

Type of Bread	Country	I've Tried It
Tortillas		
Pita Bread		
Pizza		
Baguette		

Nonfiction Reading Comprehension • 1–2 © 2005 Creative Teaching Press

Name _____ Date _____

Fill in the Bubble

Read each question. Choose the correct answer. Fill in the bubble.

1 What is the main idea of the passage about bread?
- ○ Pizza is a kind of bread.
- ○ Bread is made from flour.
- ○ Bread is eaten in countries around the world.

2 What would be another good title for this passage?
- ○ Eating Tortillas
- ○ We All Eat Bread
- ○ Breads in America

3 Which country was NOT included in the passage?
- ○ Italy
- ○ France
- ○ Sweden

4 Which fact fits with the rest of the passage?
- ○ Bread in Hong Kong can taste sweet.
- ○ Rice is eaten in many countries.
- ○ Italy has many different kinds of food.

5 What did you learn about baguettes?
- ○ You can use a baguette to make a taco.
- ○ A baguette is bread with a pocket.
- ○ Baguettes are popular in France.

6 Which sentence about tortillas is NOT true?
- ○ You can use a tortilla to make a burrito.
- ○ Tortillas are only found in Italy.
- ○ Tortillas are flat and thin.

Compass Rose

Look at any map and you will likely find a compass rose. A compass rose is a symbol that shows direction. It shows north, south, east, and west. It may also show northeast, northwest, southeast, and southwest.

When north is at the top of the compass rose, south is at the bottom. East is on the right, and west is on the left.

Northeast is between north and east. Northwest is between north and west. Can you guess where southeast and southwest are?

A compass rose gets its name because it looks like a flower. It has been used on maps since the 1300s!

The compass rose was first used to show the direction of wind. Now it shows the direction of places on a map.

Knowing the direction is very helpful when you look at a map. Suppose you leave your house and need to go across town. Do you go north or south? A map with a compass rose will tell you. Maybe you are going on a long trip. What roads do you take and which way do you turn? A map with a compass rose will tell you.

People who make maps are called **cartographers**. We already have many maps of oceans, countries, and continents. Cartographers work on maps of special areas. They might have to make new maps of places where things have changed. When a country changes its name, a new map needs to be made. When roads or landmarks move, new maps need to be made.

The next time you look at a map, find the compass rose!

Nonfiction Reading Comprehension • 1–2 © 2005 Creative Teaching Press

Make a Compass Rose

Make your own compass rose in the box. Don't forget to add the direction words!

Name _____ Date _____

Compass Rose Facts

What facts did you learn about the compass rose? Fill in the graphic organizer.

Compass Rose

Nonfiction Reading Comprehension • 1–2 © 2005 Creative Teaching Press

The Olympic Games

The Olympic Games are full of traditions. Some of these traditions started long, long ago when the first Games were played.

The first Olympic Games were held over 2,700 years ago! The only event was a <u>sprint</u>, or short run. Only men were allowed to compete in the <u>ancient</u> Olympics. The winner received a <u>wreath</u> made of olive branches, which was placed on his head. These Games were played in Greece.

The Games changed after many, many years. Many sports were added. The first year that the Games were played as they are today was in 1896, over 100 years ago. We call today's Olympics the <u>modern</u> Games.

Today, people from around the world enjoy watching the Olympics. The world's best athletes take part in the competition. The Games take place in both summer and winter. Different cities around the world <u>host</u> the Olympics. It is quite an honor to have the Olympics come to your country.

Today's winners receive a <u>medal</u>. The gold medal goes to the person who comes in first place. A silver medal is for second place, and a <u>bronze</u> medal is for third place.

The Olympic flag shows five linked rings in five colors. The rings are blue, yellow, black, green, and red. The Olympic flag was first used in 1920. It is <u>flown</u> in the city where the Games take place. When the Games are over, it is passed on to the next city that hosts the Games.

The <u>torch</u> is another special tradition of the Olympics. Each time the Olympics are played, a special torch travels around the world. The flame is always lit as the torch is passed from one person to the next. The torch makes its way to the city where the Games are being held.

Make sure to catch the next Olympic Games. When you watch the athletes today, remember that people have been competing in the Olympics for thousands of years!

Name _____ Date _____

Olympic Vocabulary

What do the words below mean? Read each sentence. Find the word from the box that fits in the blank.

ancient	bronze	flown	host	medal
modern	sprint	torch	wreath	

1 When something is old or happened in the past, it is _____.

2 Something that is shaped like
a donut and worn on your head is a _____.

3 To have the Olympics come
to your own country means to _____ the Games.

4 When something has happened recently, it is _____.

5 A special object that is given
to reward an athlete is called a _____.

6 To run very fast in a short distance is to _____.

7 When a flag is displayed, it is _____.

8 A yellowish brown color is called _____.

9 A burning stick that is held by hand is called a _____.

Nonfiction Reading Comprehension • 1–2 © 2005 Creative Teaching Press

Olympic Facts

What facts did you learn about the Olympics? Fill in the graphic organizer with one or more facts about each part of the passage.

The Olympic Games

Ancient Games	Modern Games	Olympic Flag	Olympic Torch

Ellis Island

People have been coming to America for centuries. Ellis Island was the first place many visited when they moved to the United States. These people came here from countries all around the world. They arrived on big ships.

Ellis Island is in New York Harbor. In 1892, it became an immigration station. People had to go through Ellis Island to be counted and checked. After leaving Ellis Island, people could move anywhere.

People weren't always treated very nicely during their stay on Ellis Island. They had to wait in long lines for many hours. They were tired from their long trip and scared about being in a new land. Many men traveled alone while their families stayed back home.

On Ellis Island, some people were checked to make sure they were healthy enough to live here. If not, they were turned away and not allowed to stay. Diseases spread very quickly in those days. America wanted to make sure that healthy people who were able to work were coming into the country.

This gave Ellis Island the nickname "Island of Tears." Some families had to say goodbye to each other if one member was sent home.

Today, Ellis Island is no longer an immigration station. When people come to America, they don't just come on boats. They might take a train or an airplane to get here.

Many people want to know if their families came through Ellis Island. There are old lists of those who passed through Ellis Island.

How did your family come to America? Did your family come through Ellis Island?

Nonfiction Reading Comprehension • 1–2 © 2005 Creative Teaching Press

About Ellis Island

Imagine that you had to tell someone about Ellis Island. What three things are most important to share about this place? Write the three facts on the lines.

1 _____

_____

_____

_____

2 _____

_____

_____

_____

3 _____

_____

_____

_____

Nonfiction Reading Comprehension • 1–2 © 2005 Creative Teaching Press

Name _____ Date _____

Ellis Island Facts

Read each sentence. Find the answer that makes the sentence true. Fill in the bubble.

1 Ellis Island was a(n) _____.
- ○ island in the Pacific Ocean
- ○ immigration station
- ○ ship that brought people to America

2 Ellis Island was nicknamed "Island of Tears" because _____.
- ○ family members had to say goodbye to each other if someone was sent home
- ○ people were happy to arrive in America
- ○ it was cold and windy on Ellis Island in the winter

3 People were checked for diseases on Ellis Island because _____.
- ○ medicine was kept there
- ○ America wanted healthy workers to move here
- ○ all people on ships were sick

4 At Ellis Island, people were treated badly. One example was that they had to _____.
- ○ stay for one month
- ○ find a place to live
- ○ wait in long lines

Nonfiction Reading Comprehension • 1–2 © 2005 Creative Teaching Press

Quilts

A quilt is not just like any other blanket! Quilts are very personal. They often tell a story.

People have been stitching quilts for many years. It's possible that there were people making quilts in ancient times.

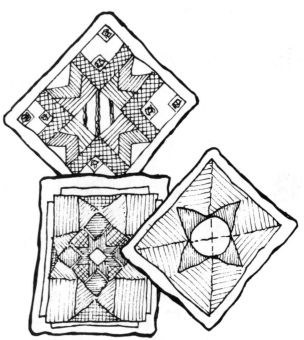

Many people in America began making quilts in the 1800s. It became very popular for women to make quilts at home. Women would also go to quilting parties and sew together. Sometimes women would go to help a friend or family member finish a quilt. This became a time for women to talk and share news about their lives.

In the past, quilts were very useful around the house. People needed big blankets to stay warm. Winters could be very cold. Quilts made people feel better at home.

A quilt often tells a story about the person who made it. Some women wrote or stitched words on the quilts they made. Others made patterns or pictures about what life was like.

Quilts can also help people feel better during a hard time. When our country fought a civil war in 1860, quilts became very important. Soldiers needed to stay warm while they were fighting the war. Women helped by making thousands of quilts. Quilts have also been made to honor someone who was very sick or died.

Today, you can find many women and men who make quilts. You might even be able to find old quilts in museums. When quilts get older, they become more fragile.

Now you understand why a quilt is more than just a blanket!

Nonfiction Reading Comprehension • 1–2 © 2005 Creative Teaching Press

Quilts Fill-In

Read each question. Choose the correct answer. Fill in the bubble.

1 What is the main idea of the passage about quilts?
- ○ Women went to quilting parties to help others sew.
- ○ You can find old quilts in a museum.
- ○ Quilts are very personal objects and often tell a story.

2 What would be a good title for this passage?
- ○ Civil War Quilts
- ○ More Than a Blanket
- ○ Men Quilt Too

3 Which fact was NOT included in the passage?
- ○ Women helped soldiers in the war by sewing quilts.
- ○ Quilts become fragile as they get older.
- ○ Quilts are always made with patterns.

4 Which fact would fit with the rest of the passage?
- ○ The Civil War was a sad time in America.
- ○ Rich and poor women made quilts in early America.
- ○ You can learn a lot when you visit a museum.

5 Which is NOT a reason why people made quilts?
- ○ People needed quilts to stay warm.
- ○ Quilts kept people safe.
- ○ Quilts can help people feel better during a hard time.

Nonfiction Reading Comprehension • 1–2 © 2005 Creative Teaching Press

Quilts Details

The main idea of the passage is that quilts are very personal objects and often tell a story. What details support that main idea? List the details on the lines.

1 _____

_____

2 _____

_____

3 _____

_____

4 _____

_____

5 _____

_____

Nonfiction Reading Comprehension • 1–2 © 2005 Creative Teaching Press

The Pony Express

When you want to send someone a letter, what do you do? You might write the letter on paper and put it in an envelope. You put a stamp on the envelope and take it to the post office. The letter is on its way! The letter might go on a car, truck, or plane. It will arrive in a few days.

Another way to send someone a letter is to use the computer. You can type a <u>message</u> in an e-mail. Once you send it, the message will reach the other person's e-mail <u>instantly</u>! That sure is fast.

How did people send mail in the past? Well, it took a lot longer back then! The Pony Express was an early kind of post office. The <u>goal</u> was to get mail from one <u>coast</u> to the other. People in California did not know about important news because mail was so slow.

About 80 young men worked for the Pony Express. They carried the mail and traveled by horse. These men were young and healthy. They had to be able to ride for long distances. They also had to be able to live through <u>harsh</u> weather. The Pony Express ran during day and night. The mail was moved in summer and winter months, too.

Each man would travel for many miles. Then he would find a new rider at the next station. The new rider would continue the <u>journey</u>.

People were very happy when the mail would finally arrive. It might have cost a lot to send a letter, but it was worth it!

The Pony Express lasted less than two years. The owners had to close it down. They did not have the money to keep it running.

Many people think the Pony Express is one of the most interesting parts of our country's history.

Nonfiction Reading Comprehension • 1–2 © 2005 Creative Teaching Press

Name _____ Date _____

The Pony Express Questions

What questions do you have about the Pony Express? List them below. Read the passage to find answers to your questions.

You might not find all your answers in the passage. Where could you go to get more information? Talk with your teacher or another adult about how to learn more about the Pony Express.

_____

_____

_____

_____

_____

_____

_____

_____

_____

_____

_____

_____

The Pony Express Vocabulary

What do these words mean? Match each word to its meaning.

1 message   trip

2 harsh   something to strive for

3 goal   note or letter

4 journey   shore

5 instantly   difficult and hard to deal with

6 coast   right away

Nonfiction Reading Comprehension • 1–2 © 2005 Creative Teaching Press

Today and the Past

Think about ways that delivering mail has changed. Fill in the chart with facts from the passage.

Sending Mail in the Past	Sending Mail Today

Name _____ Date _____

The Great Pyramids KWL

What do you know about the Great Pyramids? What do you want to know? Fill in the first two columns of the KWL chart before reading the passage. Then fill in the last column of the chart after reading the passage.

What You **K**now	What You **W**ant to Know	What You **L**earned

Nonfiction Reading Comprehension • 1–2 © 2005 Creative Teaching Press

The Great Pyramids

What a sight! The pyramids in Egypt are some of the most amazing structures on Earth.

These pyramids are <u>ancient</u>, or old. They were built over 5,000 years ago! People thought that kings, or <u>pharaohs</u>, needed a special place to rest when they died. These pyramids were made for burying kings.

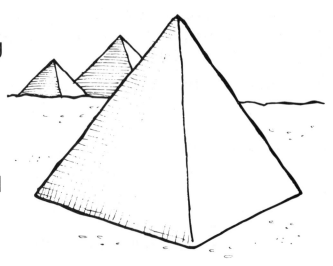

Pyramids were built while a king was still alive. Scientists have found drawings inside the pyramids. They tell about the king's life. These drawings are called <u>hieroglyphs</u>.

Other things were buried with the king's body. Jewelry and other <u>artifacts</u>, or special objects, have been found.

Many people helped build the pyramids. Scientists think that people lived in small <u>villages</u> while they were working. These villages might have had everything a worker would need to live, such as homes and bakeries.

There were other people who worked on the pyramids as well. Some helped pick the spot to build the pyramid. Others made sure the pyramid kept its shape while it was built.

The largest pyramid ever built is in Egypt. It is called the Great Pyramid. Some scientists think it took 20 years to build. It was made with over 2 million stone blocks!

People today still do not know for sure how the Great Pyramid was built. Some of the stone blocks weighed as much as 9 tons! This mystery makes the pyramids even more amazing.

You can still see the pyramids if you go to Egypt today. Many scientists from all over the world go there to study them. They are still trying to answer questions about ancient Egypt.

Nonfiction Reading Comprehension • 1–2 © 2005 Creative Teaching Press

Pyramids Sentences

Read each sentence. Use context clues to determine what the underlined word means.
Rewrite the sentence with a new word or phrase.

1 Hieroglyphs have been found in pyramids.

_____

2 Artifacts were buried with the king's body.

_____

3 The pyramids are very ancient.

_____

4 People lived in small villages while they worked on pyramids.

_____

5 People in ancient Egypt were led by pharaohs.

_____

Nonfiction Reading Comprehension • 1–2 © 2005 Creative Teaching Press

Name _____ Date _____

Pyramids Important Facts

What are the important facts you learned about pyramids? Fill in the graphic organizer.

```
                    ┌──────────────┐
                    │  The Great   │
                    │   Pyramids   │
                    └──────────────┘
```

Reasons Pyramids Were Built	People Who Built Pyramids	How Pyramids Were Built	Mysteries of the Pyramids

The Red Cross

Mother Nature often does strange things. Earthquakes, floods, and fires are just some examples of nature's power. They usually surprise us and happen very quickly.

These powerful events are called <u>natural disasters</u>. People face <u>emergencies</u> when they are not prepared for a disaster. It might be that an earthquake damages a house. Or it could be that a fire leaves a person without any home at all.

When these things happen, people need to get help. The Red Cross <u>assists</u> people when they need it.

The Red Cross works with people around the world. The American Red Cross helps us here in America. It also works with other countries.

The Red Cross will give people what they need to <u>survive</u>. It might mean that they give them a dry and safe place to sleep. They give out food and water to people who are hungry. They even have a supply of blood to help people who are <u>injured</u>.

The Red Cross does not just help those who are facing emergencies. It also gives food to the workers who come to help others.

The American Red Cross was founded by Clara Barton. She was a nurse who lived over 100 years ago. She helped soldiers who fought in the Civil War. Then she <u>created</u> the American Red Cross to help others.

The Red Cross has helped many people when they needed it most.

Nonfiction Reading Comprehension • 1–2 © 2005 Creative Teaching Press

Name _____ Date _____

The Red Cross Facts

What are the important facts of this passage? Answer the questions in complete sentences.

1 What are some examples of natural disasters?

_____

2 What does the Red Cross do?

_____

3 Where does the Red Cross help people?

_____

4 Who founded the American Red Cross?

_____

5 Why is the Red Cross so important?

_____

Nonfiction Reading Comprehension • 1–2 © 2005 Creative Teaching Press

The Red Cross Fill-In

Read each question. Choose the correct answer. Fill in the bubble.

1 What is the main idea of the passage about the Red Cross?
- ○ The Red Cross gives food to workers, too.
- ○ A fire can destroy a house.
- ○ The Red Cross helps people when they need it most.

2 What might be another good title for this passage about the Red Cross?
- ○ Helping Hands
- ○ Clara Barton to the Rescue
- ○ Watch Out for Hurricanes

3 Which fact would fit with the rest of the passage?
- ○ It is a good idea to have a disaster kit ready.
- ○ The Red Cross needs volunteers to do its work.
- ○ Clara Barton worked as a teacher.

4 What does the Red Cross NOT do for people?
- ○ give out food and water
- ○ provide a safe place to sleep
- ○ build new homes and schools

5 If this passage were longer, what else might the author write about?
- ○ what the Red Cross does in other countries
- ○ what causes a flood
- ○ what kind of food the Red Cross gives out

Nonfiction Reading Comprehension • 1–2 © 2005 Creative Teaching Press

Name _____ Date _____

The Red Cross Vocabulary

Read the six words in the word box. These are words from the passage.
Write each word in a sentence.

assists	natural disasters	created
survive	emergencies	injured

 _____

 _____

 _____

 _____

 _____

 _____

Nonfiction Reading Comprehension • 1–2 © 2005 Creative Teaching Press

Answer Key

All About Whales (page 5)

1. hair
2. pods
3. lungs
4. warm-blooded

Whale Facts (page 6)

Answers will vary. Possible answers include:
Blue Whale: biggest whale, largest animal on Earth, almost 100 feet long
Humpback Whale: about 50 feet long, loves to swim, likes to jump out of the water, gets its name from the way it moves its back when it dives
Killer Whale: also called orca, smaller than humpback whale, about 30 feet long, mostly black with white spots, eats different kinds of fish, attacks and eats young whales

Fun in the Water (page 7)

The breaching picture should show a whale jumping high out of the water.
The spyhopping picture should show a whale poking its head out of the water.
The lobtailing picture should show a whale sticking its tail out of the water.

Make a Snack (page 8)

3—Cut the fruit.
4—Mix the fruit.
1—Wash the fruit.
2—Peel the fruit.

Healthy Foods (page 9)

Answers will vary. The student's picture should include a variety of healthy foods.

From Farm to Home (page 10)

The student's pictures should match the descriptions.

All About Butterflies (page 11)

1. abdomen
2. six
3. nectar
4. all parts of the world
5. chest

Butterfly Life Cycle (page 12)

Answers may vary. Possible answers include:
First, a butterfly starts as an egg.
Then, a caterpillar or larva hatches from the egg.
Next, the larva turns into a pupa, or chrysalis.
Finally, a butterfly flies out of the chrysalis.

Monarch Butterflies (page 13)

Answers will vary. The student should fill in the KWL chart with facts and questions about monarch butterflies.

Your Five Senses (page 14)

See: picture of an eye
Feel: picture of a hand or fingers
Taste: picture of a mouth or tongue
Hear: picture of an ear
Smell: picture of a nose

Your Heart (page 15)

1. The heart is very important and it works hard to keep you healthy.
2. to make sure it is working well
3. Answers will vary.

Your Teeth (page 16)

Drawings will vary. The student's picture may indicate that brushing your teeth, going to the dentist, and eating healthy food are ways to take care of your teeth.

Your Skeleton and Bones (page 17)

1. 300
2. stand up and move around
3. calcium
4. inside your ear

Maps (page 18)

Drawings will vary. The student's picture may show a map of a classroom, a room, or another location.

South America (page 19)

Continent means a large piece of land.
Unique means interesting and different.
Mouth means the end of the river.
Borders means touches.

State Capitals (page 20)

Drawings will vary. The student's picture should illustrate a fact about your state capital or governor.

Fire Safety (page 21)

Answers will vary. Possible answers include:
1. Make sure you know how to leave your school or home.
2. It will make a loud sound if there is smoke or fire inside.
3. Stay calm if you are ever in a fire.
4. Talk to your teacher and parents to learn more that you can do in a fire.

Bicycle Safety (page 22)

Drawings will vary. Possible pictures include:
1. a bicyclist falling off a bike and bumping his or her head
2. a flat tire
3. a bicyclist riding a bike in front of cars
4. a bicyclist running over a rock or bump

Spiders (page 23)

Across
2. world
4. green
6. two

Down
1. jaws
3. legs
5. meat

Hummingbirds (page 24)

1. nectar
2. 10
3. 50
4. hovering
5. upside down
6. bugs

Camels (page 25)

Ants (page 26)

Answers will vary. Possible answers include:
Ants are strong—They can lift objects 20 times their own weight.
Ants are insects—They have six legs.
Ants live in colonies—Each colony has a queen that lays eggs.
Ants build their own homes—They dig tunnels for other ants.

Sharks (page 27)

1. O
2. F
3. O
4. F
5. F
6. O
7. F

Changing Seasons (page 28)

Drawings will vary. Possible pictures include:
Fall: raking leaves, carving a pumpkin
Winter: skiing, throwing a snowball, building a snowman
Spring: picking a flower, planting a garden, having a picnic
Summer: swimming, going to the beach

Hurricanes (page 29)

Drawings will vary. The student's picture should show a memory of a scary storm.

Measuring the Weather (page 30)

1. anemometer
2. weather map
3. barometer
4. thermometer

Grand Old Flag (page 31)

1. stripes
2. sew
3. seamstress
4. folded
5. stars

Liberty Bell (page 32)

Questions will vary. Possible questions include:
What is the Liberty Bell?
Where is the Liberty Bell located?
Why is the Liberty Bell important?
Who rings the Liberty Bell?

Do You Want to Be a Nurse? (page 33)

Drawings will vary. The student's picture may show a nurse taking a temperature, putting on a bandage, or giving medicine.

Do You Want to Be a Zoologist? (page 34)

Questions will vary. The student's questions should be related to facts that a zoologist may know about animals.

Do You Want to Be an Architect? (page 35)

An architect helps people who build homes or buildings. They draw plans to create homes, schools, and buildings. Drawings will vary.

Eric Carle (page 36)

Who? Eric Carle
What? a famous author of children's books
Where? lives in Massachusetts
When? today
Why? he loves to write books to share stories with kids

Jan Brett (page 37)

Answers will vary. Possible answers include:
Beginning: Jan Brett writing and drawing stories
Middle: Jan Brett at a museum
End: Jan Brett on a trip in a foreign place

The Long Race (page 38)

Main Idea: Runners must be very prepared to run a marathon.

Soccer (page 39)

1. football
2. goalkeeper
3. referee
4. 2

The First Flight (page 40)

Main Idea: The airplane was an important invention that changed history.

Kites (page 41)

Drawings will vary. Possible pictures include:
Kite Long Ago: a kite made of a leaf and string
Kite Today: a kite made of paper or cloth and thick string

Crayons (page 42)

Who? two cousins
What? invented crayons
Where? in New York City
When? in 1903
Why? they saw that kids needed small, safe crayons to use

Giant Pandas (page 43)

1. solitary—alone
2. endangered—a small number of an animal is alive
3. habitat—home
4. molars—teeth

Cheetahs (page 44)

Answers will vary. Possible facts include:
fastest mammals on Earth, can run up to 70 miles an hour, great eyesight, has many spots, are endangered

Sea Turtles (page 45)

1. warm sea
2. scaly
3. swimmers, divers
4. crabs, shrimp, sea life
5. endangered

The Sun (page 46)

S	O	L	A	R	S	Y	S	T	E	M
A	S	T	Y	S	U	N	V	K	L	J
G	I	T	R	P	M	R	N	E	C	S
D	A	L	A	X	D	O	L	Y	H	T
L	C	A	P	P	D	E	N	C	O	A
U	L	I	M	O	P	H	E	A	T	R
E	A	R	T	H	L	I	E	R	H	L

Saturn (page 47)

Answers will vary. Possible facts include:
the sixth planet from the sun, has rings around it, has many moons, second-largest planet in the solar system

Asteroids and Comets (page 48)

Asteroids: made of rock and metal, can be small or large
Comets: made of gas and ice, have a head and a tail
Both: in space, orbit the sun

Ocean Life (page 49)

1. T
2. F
3. T
4. F
5. T
6. F

Tide Pools (page 50)

Main Idea: Tide pools are home to plants and animals that must be able to survive many changes.

Pollution (page 51)

Drawings will vary. The student's picture may show someone picking up trash on the beach, recycling, or riding a bike instead of driving in a car.

George Washington (page 52)

1. live in the White House
2. Abraham Lincoln
3. President of the United States
4. strong leader
5. February

Dr. Seuss (page 53)

The student should fill in the KWL chart with facts and questions about Dr. Seuss.

Jackie Robinson (page 54)

Who? Jackie Robinson
What? the first African American to play baseball in the major leagues
Where? in Brooklyn
When? in 1947
Why? to show people that African Americans should be allowed to play sports

Sally Ride (page 55)

Answers will vary. Possible answers include:
When she was young, Sally wanted to be a tennis player.
When she was older, Sally wanted to train to be an astronaut.
In 1983, Sally went into space.
Today, Sally helps girls do well in science and math.

Deserts (page 56)

Answers will vary. Possible facts include:
usually very hot; can get very cold, too; many plants and animals live in the desert; largest desert is in Africa

Rain Forests (page 57)

Drawings will vary. The student's picture may show: someone recycling or conserving paper.

Grasslands (page 58)

Answers will vary. Possible answers include:
1. climate—weather
2. frigid—very cold
3. graze—eat
4. content—happy
5. herds—groups of animals

Tundra (page 59)

The student should fill in the KWL chart with facts and questions about the tundra.

The White House (page 60)

1. President's House
2. Washington, D.C.
3. Oval Office
4. 132
5. 2

Mount Rushmore (page 61)

1. sculpture—statue or monument
2. carve—shape into an object
3. enormous—very large
4. tribute—honor or compliment

The Golden Gate Bridge (page 62)

1. picture of no bridge
2. picture of bridge, half completed
3. picture of bridge with a few cars
4. picture of bridge with many cars and bikes crossing

Family of Instruments (page 64)

Answers will vary. Possible answers include:
String Family: have strings, played with hands or bow, a violin belongs in this family

Woodwind Family: most are made of wood, need breath to make a sound, a clarinet belongs in this family

Brass Family: made of brass or other metal, have long tubes, horns, tuba is in this family

Percussion Family: keep the beat for the rest of the band, people hit or shake them to make noise, drums and cymbals are in this family

Orchestra Vocabulary (page 65)

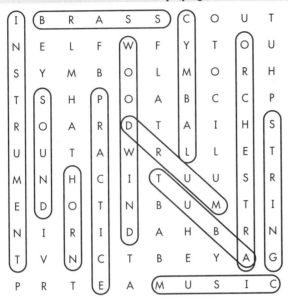

Traveling (page 67)

Answers will vary. Possible answers include:
1. a bike
2. because they had no pedals
3. there were few cars on the road to worry about
4. a scooter
5. there are so many cars to watch out for
6. scooters are made to go fast

Transportation Changes (page 68)

Answers will vary. Possible answers include:
Transportation in the Past: took a long time, people rode horses, horses pulled wagons, trains were better than horses
Transportation Today: trips are faster, space shuttles take people to space, easier to get around, more cars

Columbus Timeline (page 70)

Answers will vary. Possible answers include:
1451: Christopher Columbus was born in Italy
1492: Christopher Columbus sailed to the New World
After 1492: Christopher Columbus returned to the New World three more times

Columbus Main Idea (page 71)

1. Main Idea: Christopher Columbus was a brave sailor who discovered a new world.
2. Answers will vary.

Fossils Graphic Organizer (page 73)

Answers will vary. Possible facts include:
can be proof of an animal or a plant, can be the hard part of the animal or plant, paleontologists look for fossils, fossils need to be collected carefully, fossils can be found anywhere

What Happens to Fossils? (page 74)

2—Part of the plant or animal is buried.
6—Once the fossil is found, it is washed and identified.
3—The plant or animal hardens over time and becomes a rock.
1—A plant or an animal dies.
7—After scientists know what the fossil is, they try to find out how old it is.
5—Scientists discover the fossil.
4—Scientists dig for fossils.

Taking Care of a Garden (page 76)

Answers will vary. Possible answers include:
Plant things in the sun, find good soil, water plants when they are dry, pull weeds, plant the right kinds of plants

Working in a Garden (page 77)

Answers will vary. Possible pictures may include:
1. a plant that is larger and has grown from being watered
2. plants that are growing too close together
3. a garden without weeds

Taking Care of Our Planet (page 79)

Answers will vary. The student's picture may show a school or park full of litter, a dirty beach, smoggy or polluted air, or dead trees.

Planet Problems (page 80)

Answers will vary. The student's writing should describe a local environmental problem and a way to fix it.

Comparing Volcanoes (page 82)

Answers will vary. Possible answers include:
Extinct Volcano: will not erupt again
Dormant Volcano: has not erupted in thousands of years, but it is not extinct
Active Volcano: might erupt, so people watch it

Volcano Crossword (page 83)

Across
1. layers
5. lava
6. water

Down
2. geologists
3. ash
4. Hawaii
7. erupt

Computer Rules (page 85)

Answers will vary. Possible answers include:
no eating or drinking near the computer, don't hit or slam the keyboard, sit properly in front of the computer, sit up straight with your feet on the floor, never give out personal information, keep your password a secret

Is It True? (page 86)

1. T
2. F
3. F
4. T
5. F
6. F
7. F
8. T

What Do You Want to Know? (page 88)

Answers will vary. Possible questions include:
Who built the Great Wall of China?
When was the Great Wall of China built?
Why was a wall built?
What is it used for today?

What Does It Mean? (page 89)

1. span—extend across
2. invaders—people who want to attack
3. legend—story that may or may not be true
4. emperors—leaders
5. orbiting—revolving around
6. landmark—special place
7. astronauts—travelers in a spacecraft
8. structure—something built

Word Meaning (page 91)

Answers will vary. Possible answers include:
1. pack—a group of animals
2. endangered—there are few of a specific kind of animal
3. steam—water in the form of gas
4. geyser—water that is pushed into the air
5. cubs—young bears
6. bison—a mammal also called a buffalo
7. survive—remain alive

Yellowstone Sentences (page 92)

Answers will vary. The student's sentences should include each vocabulary word in an appropriate context.

Bread (page 94)

Country
Tortillas—Mexico
Pita Bread—Isreal
Pizza—Italy
Baguette—France

I've Tried It
Answers will vary.

Fill in the Bubble (page 95)

1. Bread is eaten in countries around the world.
2. We All Eat Bread
3. Sweden
4. Bread in Hong Kong can taste sweet.
5. Baguettes are popular in France.
6. Tortillas are only found in Italy.

Make a Compass Rose (page 97)

The student's picture should show a compass rose that is correctly labeled.

Compass Rose Facts (page 98)

Answers will vary. Possible facts include:
a symbol, shows direction, gets its name because it looks like a flower, has been used on maps since the 1300s, first used to show the direction of wind

Olympic Vocabulary (page 100)

1. ancient
2. wreath
3. host
4. modern
5. medal
6. sprint
7. flown
8. bronze
9. torch

Olympic Facts (page 101)

Answers will vary. Possible facts include:
Ancient Games: held over 2,700 years ago, only event was a sprint, only men were allowed to compete, winner received a wreath made of olive branches which was placed on his head, games were played in Greece

Modern Games: take place in both summer and winter, different cities around the world host, winners are given a medal

Olympic Flag: shows five linked rings in five colors, first used in 1920

Olympic Torch: travels around the world, passed from one person to the next, makes its way to the city where the games are

About Ellis Island (page 103)

Answers will vary. Possible answers include:
Ellis Island was an immigration station.
People had to be counted and checked at Ellis Island when they came to the United States.
People were often treated poorly on Ellis Island.
People were checked for diseases before they were allowed to stay.
Families sometimes had to say goodbye to each other if one person was sent home.

Ellis Island Facts (page 104)

1. immigration station
2. family members had to say goodbye to each other if someone was sent home
3. America wanted healthy workers to move here
4. wait in long lines

Quilts Fill-In (page 106)

1. Quilts are very personal objects and often tell a story.
2. More Than a Blanket
3. Quilts are always made with patterns.
4. Rich and poor women made quilts in early America.
5. Quilts kept people safe.

Quilts Details (page 107)

Answers will vary. Possible answers include:
Some women wrote or stitched words on the quilts they made.
Some women made patterns or pictures in their quilts about what life was like.
Women stitched quilts to help soldiers in the Civil War.
Quilts kept people warm and made them feel better.

The Pony Express Questions (page 109)

Answers will vary. Possible questions include:
What was the Pony Express?
Who started the Pony Express?
When was the Pony Express working?
Why did the Pony Express stop working?

The Pony Express Vocabulary (page 110)

1. message—note or letter
2. harsh—difficult and hard to deal with
3. goal—something to strive for
4. journey—trip
5. instantly—right away
6. coast—shore

Today and the Past (page 111)

Answers will vary. Possible answers include:

Sending Mail in the Past: took a long time, cost a lot of money, or done by horse

Sending Mail Today: easy, arrives quickly, cheap, done by plane or car, e-mail sends letters instantly

The Great Pyramids KWL (page 112)

Answers will vary. The student should fill in the KWL chart with facts and questions about pyramids.

Pyramids Sentences (page 114)

Answers will vary. Possible answers include:

1. Drawings have been found in pyramids.
2. Special objects were buried with the king's body.
3. The pyramids are very old.
4. People lived in small towns while they worked on pyramids.
5. People in ancient Egypt were led by kings.

Pyramids Important Facts (page 115)

Answers will vary. Possible answers include:

Reasons Pyramids Were Built: to give kings a special place to rest after death

People Who Built Pyramids: all different kinds of people

How Pyramids Were Built: people worked together for many years

Mysteries of the Pyramids: how people lifted heavy rocks, how the Great Pyramid was built

The Red Cross Facts (page 117)

Answers will vary. Possible answers include:
1. Some examples of natural disasters are earthquakes, floods, and fires.
2. The Red Cross helps people who face natural disasters.
3. The Red Cross helps people all over the world.
4. Clara Barton founded the American Red Cross.
5. The Red Cross is so important because it helps people when they need it most.

The Red Cross Fill-In (page 118)

1. The Red Cross helps people when they need it most.
2. Helping Hands
3. The Red Cross needs volunteers to do its work.
4. build new homes and schools
5. what the Red Cross does in other countries

The Red Cross Vocabulary (page 119)

Sentences will vary. The student's sentences should include each vocabulary word in an appropriate context.